A Nest of Teachers

EDWARD BLISHEN

A Nest of Teachers

HAMISH HAMILTON
LONDON

First published in Great Britain 1980
by Hamish Hamilton Limited
Garden House 57–59 Long Acre London WC2E 9JZ

Copyright © 1980 by Edward Blishen

British Library Cataloguing in Publication Data

Blishen, Edward
    A nest of teachers.
    1. Education – England 2, Teaching
    I. Title
    371. 1'0092'4   LA631.82
    ISBN 0–241–10145–X

Printed in Great Britain by
Bristol Typesetting Co. Ltd,
Barton Manor, St Philips, Bristol

To HARRY RÉE
with love and amusement

PART ONE

1

I was on my way to be emergency-trained. It would have seemed, only a few years before, an odd thing to be embarked upon. How easily, I thought as I approached Isleden Emergency Training College that morning in the midsummer of 1949—how easily and placidly one became accustomed to jargon. Had I ever really wondered about the term 'emergency'? That was a rawly dramatic word—there ought to be sirens, lights flashing, hoarse voices shouting instructions. The emergency, of course, was the drastic post-war need for teachers. The paralysis of conventional training during the war years had made it necessary to drum up new teachers in a hurry—and to look for them in uncommon corners.

We'd be ex-servicemen: also, further back, ex-bank clerks, insurance clerks, policemen, shopkeepers. People who, their first choice of occupation interrupted by war, had thought again.

Thought? Had I truly thought about being a teacher?

Kate had said, when I left our flat that morning: 'Now you have what you want. Now you can learn to be something you've decided to become.'

Kate's shining eyes. Kate's anxiety to represent me to myself in a simple, splendid light. Her words had triggered off the guilty impatience I'd felt so often during our first year of marriage. I couldn't be—but oh, how I wished I could be—as straightforward and fine as she saw me. I hadn't the faintest resolution to follow some line of occupation. I'd drifted, three years before, into being a prep school teacher, massively unqualified. From that, by some similar principle of pure drift, I'd been swept into this bewildered course of presenting myself as a candidate for emergency training. But I was as uncertain about teaching as I was about marriage.

3

I was, come to think of it (and I hoped Kate might never know I'd thought of it), being emergency-trained as a husband.

Our flat. Mrs Nape, our landlady, meeting us infallibly on the stairs of a morning—carrying, at arm's length, her unashamed pot of urine. 'I've just heard,' she would say, 'from my son, Frederick. He has been appointed to a new post. He is ADC to the General. He needs another uniform. Well, you know, he is six foot three and a half inches in his socks . . .'

Kate and I would stiffen against our longing to laugh, wildly. Mrs Nape never mentioned her son Frederick—and he was her main topic—without referring (with that precision, and always with that glance at his socks) to his height. In occupying the upper floor of her house, we had become those to whom she could talk about Frederick. He frowned down at us, from a very tall picture-frame (but wearing boots), as we lay in bed. It had been clear that Mrs Nape would have been most disobliged had we taken him down—replaced him, perhaps, as Kate longed to do, with Van Gogh sunflowers. We sometimes turned his face to the wall, uneasy about that furious military glare.

I drove Major Nape out of my mind's eye and gave my attention to the building I was approaching.

Isleden was housed in a Working Men's Institute of some historical fame, established in the last century. Victorian idealism had shaped the place, which had a bulky, red-brick confidence. Up the main steps now were going . . . oh, in general, it seemed to be briefcases, moustaches. I felt slightly absurd as I joined them, as you feel when entering a new place among strangers to whom it's equally new. That awkward desire to seem at ease, and shame at feeling it. Shyness mixed with curiosity. Some extra mortification, perhaps, because we did seem to be carrying very much the same briefcase, and many were wearing fairly inter-changeable moustaches.

Kate had said: 'You will make new friends, and they'll stimulate you. Oh, you know you'll be glad of that!'

Of course, Kate was right; and of course, she was wrong. One of the problems of these early months of marriage was that Kate turned out to have this gift of saying what was, simultaneously, perfectly true and completely false. I *was* looking forward to new friendships, and I did hope for stimulation. But Kate, oh dear Kate, made it sound as though I was filled with exultation at the

4

prospect. There I was, out to make friends! I wasn't; I was creeping up those steps in a mass of strangers, terrified by the idea of the labour and self-adjustment involved in getting to know them. Too much human novelty—far too much!

'Assemble,' said a notice inside the door, 'in the Hall.' An arrow pointed.

I thought, resolutely, of the distinguished philanthropists who had ordained the existence of this building. The monumental art critic, the socialist parson, the great mid-Victorian melancholy poet . . .

The hall filled with repetitive moustaches.

And silence. On the platform, the principal had risen to address us.

Mr Trellis, who was to superintend our transformation into teachers, was tall, grey-haired, with the sort of gentle, sonorous voice that proclaims a desire to *ennoble* everything. It was a preacher's voice. He had a preacher's gestures, too: they began at his bosom, to suggest that this was the source from which his words were being collected, and then became great sweeps of the arms, distinctly agricultural: he was broadcasting the words among us, like a sower. 'It is for a great adventure we are gathered here'—the words were flung among us: he turned this way and that, to ensure a fair scattering—'what I hope will be a splendid adventure, for us all . . .'

After five wartime years on the land, I was sensitive to agricultural images. I pursued them as I listened. Here, perhaps, at last, in the course of this, hmm, great adventure, I would be learning something, systematically. The muddy flood of my interests would be given a channel, banks, a direction. My intellect would be ditched, hedged, sown and cropped. I examined hopefully the agriculturalists who would conduct this operation: the lecturers surrounding Mr Trellis on the platform. Hmm. More moustaches.

Largely information as to the way we should be divided up. Alphabetically, into tiny tutorial groups. According to choices of main study, into other groups. Timetables. 'Please, gentlemen, make careful notes. It is rather complicated.' It was. I was glad when the information—it was like being briefed for everlasting-ness—was brought to a temporary halt.

5

We met in our alphabetical tutorials. Twelve people united by
having names that began with B or C. The tutor's name began
with S. Mr Salt had shy amused eyes and rubbed himself against
the wall as he talked. One afternoon soon we were going, as
alphabetical tutorials, to various events on offer in London.
This experience, it was hoped, would bring us together. It would
be like the sort of outings on which we might take children. Mr
Trellis had suggested Westminster Abbey for our group : but Mr
Salt hoped to persuade him that we should go, instead, to the
exhibition of Rubens and Velasquez then at the Tate Gallery.
Mr Salt rubbed himself against the wall. 'I think we might find
the painters . . . more stimulating.' He hastened to add that he
did not mean that visiting Westminster Abbey was a vacuous
experience. 'But the painters might be less familiar?' The
tutorial, altogether shy, wriggled its agreement.

Back to the bulging hall. And here, very quickly, as the platform discussed income tax, grants, allowances, and similar
matters that made me think guiltily of Kate—did she really, after
a year of marriage, understand that I was a financial fool?—
here, at once, the dominant characters of the course declared
themselves. How odd, the cookery of any group, so assembled!
To the top of the pot rise quickly the unabashed, the exhibi-
tionists, the useful persons, the seekers after power. There was to
be a students' union, and it was to have officers. Possible officers
emerged, instantly. There were bewildering preludes to election :
nominations, proposals as to a ballot . . . Colourful persons rose
and made colourful assertions. Mr Salt, I noticed, robbed of a
wall to rub himself against, rubbed himself against his chair. At
intervals, Mr Trellis rose, scattered noble ideas. Mr Jepp, who
was to be in charge of Education—a special sub-division? was it
not *all* a matter of education?—also rose : a man clearly intended
by the great pattern-maker to act as a balance to Mr Trellis. Mr
Trellis sowed his grand seeds of nobility : Mr Jepp, who had
enormous and mischievous eyes, sowed seeds of another kind :
brutally practical. 'You're all,' he said, ' entertaining ideas that
are beside the point. Don't ask how I know : I've seen thousands
of you in my time. I'm here to nip your idealism in the bud. I'm
here to keep your noses to the grindstone and your eyes on the
goal.' Former soldiers among us obviously recognised him as the
sergeant-major of the course. Habituated growls and groans of

practical assent rose from all quarters of the hall. Mr Jepp was a startling success. Amid all the nobility of things, he was offering backbone, substance, drill.

The vice-principal rose. He was at once, it appeared, psychology and religion. He was avuncular, large: an educational bishop. He seemed to bridge the interesting gulf between Mr Trellis and Mr Jepp. I recognised the manner: we'd had such a leader in the Crusaders, a curious alternative to Sunday School for boys from superior schools. I'd belonged to it, with dismayed brevity, when I was fourteen. The manner was hearty: it suggested at once the man of the world and the man a little bit out of it. Lofty practicality, airy down-to-earthness. 'You chaps', he called us. I thought that, in the agricultural aspect of things, he'd be like those wartime officials who enthusiastically led us astray as to the digging of ditches. The water would always, in an atmosphere of very cheerful astonishment, run the wrong way.

We broke for tea. There were counters that opened up, revealing desperate-looking women, who made available desperate-looking tea. I found myself alongside Mr Bing and Mr Broom, both from my optional tutorial. Mr Bing was neat and dark, with hair laid back in shining wings: he talked neatly, too, in a tentatively sceptical tone. 'There's going to be rather a lot of rather fine talk?' More question than statement: and a small smile that was itself questioning. Mr Broom was neat and fair and given to self-disparagement: 'I can tell you straightaway that I'm worried about a course that makes room for me.' Biographies were exchanged with amazing fullness. Mr Bing had been in the Army: Mr Broom in the RAF. Both were mathematicians: and both were divorced. Both, in a rather pessimistic way, had mistresses . . . 'My goodness,' I said. 'I feel terribly respectable.' Mr Broom looked at me, with great deliberation, up and down. 'You're the intelligentsia,' he said. 'Middle class intelligentsia. Very settled nature. The emotional cream. Lucky chap.' It was totally untrue. I was lower middle class, emotionally all over the place: my family had tried quite hard to change my mind about having a mind. But I beamed.

Back in the hall we elected the officers of the Students' Union. Then to a room where the Government presented me with a voucher for £94, on which Kate and I and our

7

baby-in-the-making would live for the coming quarter: and home.

'I think,' I told Kate, 'that I am going to enjoy this course.'
But the effect of that long first day of my official approach to teacherhood was that I could not relax, could not sit down, could not be calm. '*Please*,' said Kate, and then noticed the anguish in her voice and said it again, 'please just sit with me and be happy.' Well, I *was* happy. But oh, on the brink of learning, for the first time, to be a specific sort of person, what uneasy happiness it was! I thought, looking at Kate's anxious face, that it was much the same sort of uncomfortable and unfamiliar happiness that our marriage had provided.

2

'What we have to learn to do,' said Mr Trellis on the second morning, 'is to open windows in the souls of the children we teach.'

As he said this, he slowly spread out his very long arms. He had in mind, clearly, no ordinary fenestration. These were French windows, at least. A shy smile was instantly corrected by an expression of total gravity. 'We must bring sweetness and light into their lives.'

He was followed by Mr Jepp, who merely wished to say that he'd been short of one or two persons in his optional tutorial the day before, and that if they did not appear that afternoon he would take them apart in a very slow and cruel manner.

'Do you think they work this out together?' Bing whispered. That seemed unlikely; but the perfectly amiable contradiction of Trellis by Jepp, and the other way round (their good relations were evident from the smiles they exchanged, a friendly swopping of the gentle for the fierce), was to become the mark of the whole of that year of training. Encouraged to take a noble view of our work as teachers, we were also to be warned against too fine an outlook. Anxiously we were to move between the notion of opening theoretical windows, and a counter-notion of keeping actual windows free from breakage.

There occurred during this second day an activity with the character of some great spontaneous folk movement: the forming of societies. I had not guessed that a newly-gathered body of people would divide up at once according to hobbies, faiths, politics and much else. There were photographers who could not exist without banding together with other photographers: cricketers, geographers, fencers ('Single combat with foil, épée or sabre provides thrills and satisfies the sporting urge while demanding full co-ordination of mind and body', said, terrifyingly, their recruiting notice), Christians, socialists, Christian socialists, ramblers . . . the college seethed with groups being formed, with chairmen, secretaries and treasurers being appointed. I was hesitantly drawn to the Literary Society, but arrived at the first meeting to hear someone declare that there was nothing remotely difficult about *Finnegans Wake*. 'I read it again and again,' he said, as if he had been speaking of *Wizard* or *Beano*. I thought this was too much and tiptoed away to the Dramatic Society. 'Who,' the question was being asked, 'will be chairman?' Desperate modesty reigned: and during the brief moment that it did so, on an impulse quite unrelated to character —I had been all set to go through life totally without office—my hand raised itself. There was a smilingly crestfallen acceptance of my offer, and there I was: Chairman of the Isleden Emergency Training College Dramatic Society. (CIETCDS, for short, if one ever came round to that.) At once I found my veins flooded with authoritarian juices, and had a secretary and treasurer elected, and had brought about our affiliation with the British Drama League, before my slaves could draw breath. I also heard myself recommend that thought be given to the choice of a play, to be performed—arrogantly I turned the pages of my diary—in four months' time. Feeling very much as I would have done if I were being hoisted into a palanquin by a team of Nubians, I declared the meeting over and left the room, trembling with the unlikelihood of it all.

What I was chiefly moved by at this point was the thought of the curious oddity of our all being there to be made into teachers. To begin with, we were so dissimilar. There ought, surely, to be some common factor in any group of men who'd elected, especially so deliberately, to become instructors of the young. Something, perhaps, like some hint of a family resemblance in the face. But I had never been subjected to such a nerve-racking experience of sheer facial difference. Again that curious feeling, when you enter fresh among a whole body of strangers! I began to cease to take even my own face for granted. Such variations on the simple theme of the human nose! And given the limits of the possible distance between nose and upper lip, anything in excess of which would produce monstrosity, how different from each other people were made by a millimetre more or less in that area!

And we were all going to be teachers! At times I had a feeling that resolved itself idiotically into an impulse of pity for children. Here, under Mr Trellis's leadership, so romantic, and Mr Jepp's, perfectly cynical, we were being trained for our invasion of the schools. Weapon training . . .

Well, the nature of the weapons wasn't yet obvious. It looked —and I froze at the thought—as though *visual aids* were to rank high among them. It was a newish term, in 1949, with a menacing successor already in the wings : *audio*-visual aids. There was, when things really got under way, to be a regular lecture on these aids. We would be encouraged in the making of models, and instructed in the use of film projectors, epidiascopes and other machinery. As someone who had achieved in the model-making field, in the twenty-nine years of his life, one hand-carved wooden travesty of the 1931 Schneider-trophy-winning seaplane—a model in which the floats kept breaking away, the two-inch nails by which they were secured to the fuselage simply dropping out if the model were merely glanced at—I did not look forward to visual aids. I hoped it might be thought that there were other pedagogic weapons in the use of which one could be satisfactorily trained.

It was, however, for the moment, all preparation. We made notes about the making of notes; and timetables, paving the way for timetables. We met the men, and the woman or two, who would polish up our science, art, biology, botany, mathematics.

Many of them seemed determined to secure our approval by a persistent jocularity. They made jokes intended to take all seriousness out of things. As a joker in search of seriousness, I felt uneasy. It was a relief to have a first lecture from Mr Strike, History, that was a simple, straightforward, perfectly unamusing history lesson. On no easily discernible principle, Mr Strike had decided to return us to the fall of the Roman Empire as a taking-off point for our flight through time: and he employed that most familiar of visual aids, an extremely tatty blackboard. On this, with disrespect for the work of centuries of geographers, he roughed out a map of Europe, and rapidly increased the difficulty of understanding him by filling this map with arrows. These represented the barbarians as they converged on Rome. I found the experience enormously refreshing and useful. For the first time as an adult, I was subjected to one of the favourite teaching techniques of my own schooldays: and understood how appalling it was. Once again—here was the nub of Roman history, as we'd known it—the arrows from the top left-hand corner of the blackboard, and those from the top right-hand corner, joined with those rising indiscriminately from the bottom of the blackboard, to destroy the civilisation in the centre of the blackboard. To this account of The Decline and Fall of the Centre of the Blackboard, Mr Strike added one rather embarrassing peculiarity of his own. He made us personally responsible for the historical forces engaged. That's to say, he would talk about 'your Goths' and 'your Romans'. 'So when your Goths and your Visigoths and your Vandals and your Huns began pouring into your Rome, then your Romans had their backs to the wall in earnest . . .' It was a relief to discover that we were not responsible for the wall.

3

We were given a General Knowledge test. Not difficult. Well, for example, in a list of names to which we had to attach achievements and rough dates, there was the name of Chiffley. The early nineteenth century landscape painter. A miniaturist, on the whole. I could see his paintings very clearly, as I filled in my answer. Small, crustily green and brown : tarns mostly, high on hills. Welsh hills. The familiar signature in the corner : Chiffley, 1807 . . .

I gave up my paper and realised at once that Chiffley was the current Prime Minister of Australia. So far as I knew, he'd never painted a picture in his life.

I expected instant dismissal from the course. Mr Trellis would say : 'I'm very sorry indeed, but I'm sure you will understand that we cannot send people into the schools who are not only ignorant of current affairs but are inclined to fill the gaps in their knowledge with . . . fantasy.' Charmingly he would shake my hand and pass me over to Mr Jepp, who would kick me down the college steps.

Throughout the course there were moments when I confidently expected expulsion. I was even, in some rigorous corner of my soul, dismayed that it did not take place. I would have felt, absurdly, more worthy to be a teacher if I'd been told that I was unfitted to be one. It took me a long time to realise that quite sensational defects were necessary if one had dismissal in mind.

'Optional' was the term for the single-subject study you'd chosen to follow. I was Optional Literature. In time this was rubbed down to Op Lit 1. This first of three groups, I was delighted to discover, was in the charge of Mr Salt.

We were required, he told us, to choose and undertake a special study—a sort of Optional Optional. He wouldn't call this a thesis, though some people (he rubbed an area of the wall quite bare) did talk in such terms. He hoped a better account of it would be an enjoyable obsession.

Suppressing a nervous sense of the pretentiousness of making any choice—there were chaps who were lifting Chaucer or Wordsworth or Coleridge on to their shoulders, and one man was going to distinguish between The Sixteen Faces of Ernest Hemingway—I chose John Donne. Mr Salt said : 'Oh good. Have you a special focus?' Then, when I looked blank : 'There usually has to be some sort of reason given, true or false, for wanting to read and think about a favourite poet.' 'Ah,' I said. 'Perhaps one could inquire why he has such a strong hold on twentieth century imagination?' 'Perfect,' said Mr Salt : sounding like the boss of some thieves' kitchen, rehearsing his men in aliases and alibis.

As an alphabetical tutorial, Salt's men went to the Tate Gallery for the exhibition of paintings by Rubens and Velasquez. We were to report back on what we'd seen. Assigned to the Rubens room, which gave the impression of being on fire, there was so much glowing red, Bing and I halted in front of a large allegorical painting of the four continents. These were represented by women—though somehow 'ladies' seemed to be the word—of a strength and comeliness befitting the large and fruitful areas they symbolised. Beside each of them squatted a comparably strong, silver-haired man, the fertilising river of each continent. They sat there, under the world's awning (an actual silken roof), engaged in some sort of midsummer conversation. At least—were they conversing? Difficult to tell : but there was a hint, in the way they leaned together, of inter-continental tittle-tattle. Or rather, it seemed to be a pause in such an exchange, and the black lady who represented Africa, for one, was looking in a startled way out of the canvas, as if about to inform the Nile that she was being stared at by Bing and me.

'Extraordinary,' said Bing. 'Such nonsense. As a dialectical materialist, I think I'm offended. But they are so real, don't you think? I have this strong feeling that I once knew Asia quite well, and behaved rather badly to her.'

And animals, so gloriously painted ! Such complexity and rich-

13

ness! The most unlikely colours combined in small bold slashes and whirls to compose, if one stood back only a foot or so, as leonine a lion as could be wished.

'Do you realise,' said Bing, 'that the Government is actually paying us for looking closely at this lion?'

And at *The Feast of Venus*. Rubens' inimitable babies, unmistakable ladies. In the centre, a statue of Venus. Women pressing offerings upon her. Centre foreground, lively little groups of children: those deliciously plump, solemn or impish-faced infants of whom both Venus and Rubens were so fond. They were, as Bing observed, absolute non-schoolchildren. In the bottom corners, women advancing eagerly towards the statue, bearing little replicas of themselves. For the chief lady, a gift of ladies . . . Above the statue, cherubs swimming in loops through the trees; and behind them all, a never-never landscape, a dream of ideal greenness, and the uncleaned but still vivid blue of sky. In 1949, Rubens was an implicit riposte to the austerity of the times. Just to look at him was to commit treason. He was sedition and heresy in the form of plumpness and high colouring and reckless fruitfulness.

'A little paganism is good for everyone, and it seems a pity that a Rubens can't be hung somewhere in every school—and I guess, after that visit, I mean an original Rubens,' said Bing, reporting back on our behalf to the tutorial. Mr Salt said he was glad he'd not heard this tempting comment a few years earlier. 'It was bad enough fighting for a mere extension of secondary education . . .'

Bing had been specially moved by the thought that he wasn't going to be teaching Rubens' chubby children. I was less regretful, because I felt certain I *was* going to teach the proletarian equivalents of Velasquez's little princes and princesses, staring out at the world in such a queer, wooden, half-shy, half-sullen way. I thought it best not to tell Bing, who could be very formally Marxist, that I liked the Spanish royal face. Or I thought I did so. I even liked the Infanta Margarita Teresa, whose face was so very long and plain, whose cheeks were so uncharmingly red. Was it their reality that made them so likeable? Elsewhere in the room were other royal portraits by other hands. Skilful elaboration of rich gowns and cloaks, detailed lifelikeness of face. If detail could create reality, they should have been ten times as real as Velasquez's infantas. Yet all that smooth clever paint only mummified the royal sitters, whereas Velasquez, with his queer immediacy of manner, painted as if it had all been done this morning. Something there about the nature of reality? The deadening effect of an unselective approach to detail?

Bing and I gave ourselves a fierce inward shaking, leaving the Tate. What had all that to do with being a teacher-in-training? Long afterwards we looked back and saw that it had more to do with it than much that happened at Isleden during the course. As Bing was to say, when it was all over—perhaps if for a year we'd done nothing much but go to galleries and peer closely at pictures, we might have been quite remarkably *better* prepared to teach.

4

As it was, we were to be invited to peer closely at the reality of the schools, in three days of observation.

There were two ways of looking at a visit of observation to a school. For us, it was designed as an occasion when we could watch teachers at work, and profit from doing so. For the teachers, it was capable of being seen as the unnerving intrusion into their classroom of young spies who'd sit making notes—almost certainly, loftily and ignorantly critical ones.

Mr Jepp made this the subject of one of his fiercest talks. 'For God's sake,' he groaned, 'show some discretion! Don't criticise! If a teacher says to you, "The Head is nuts," don't say, " Nuts isn't the word for him!" Look at him blankly and say "Indeed!" If you don't, sure enough it'll get back to the Head. The teacher won't mean any harm. He'll just say to the Head in passing: "Cocky young chap, that, from Isleden! I happened to be making an ordinary remark about how brilliantly the school is organised, and he said "Nuts!" ' Mr Jepp gave one of his glares, already famous : they both expressed delight at the laughter he caused, and set out to douse it. 'And don't dash into the staffroom rubbing your hands and say : "Well, those kids have learned more in ten minutes than they've learned in the last ten years!" Go about like *mice*! Come on! Try it! All look at me like *mice*!'

The college did its best. It fixed the platform with mild pink smiles. Students here and there twitched notional whiskers : there was a squeak or two. 'Some of you,' Jepp raged, 'I'd have been glad to have over a desk, twenty years ago, when I might just possibly have been able to influence your characters for good.'

And so, in the company of a student called Mince, I found myself at Green Rise Secondary Modern. I suppose this suburban corner had at one time been that gentle thing, a rise, and green with it. Now it was a grey mess of small houses and shops groaning up a slope. The school was at the top. It, too, was very grey.

The Head had forgotten we were coming. 'Ah, yes,' he said. 'Well, we'll fix something.' He stared hard at Mince—as I had done, when we met outside the school gates. It was obvious from the start that Mince was one of those students who would not last the course. Indeed, it was clear that he did not intend to do so. I don't know how such applicants were ever accepted for training : except, of course, that too many had to be seen by vastly overbusy sparetime selection boards. There were half a dozen such men at Isleden—natural drifters, doomed choppers and changers, who would all their lives begin things, and carry nothing to a conclusion. Mince caused me to stare at him because he wore, and rarely took off, long motorcyclists' gloves. There was also his attitude, which was that of a man convinced that only by the exercise of a tireless tetchy suspicion could he protect himself from being infamously deceived and exploited. He said now, clapping his gloves together as he did so: 'We were told the schools would have programmes worked out for us.' I wondered how mouse-like I would have to be to counter the impact of this rogue elephant.

Green Rise seemed a brisk school. Enter a classroom, and the children would leap up and stand by their desks till told to sit.

16

I spent the first morning with one of the oldest members of the staff, who'd been there since 1913. The essential part of his face, the part that defined him, was remarkably small, compressed between high forehead and fleshy chin. In every respect, he was amazingly inexpressive. Flat, mild, running on some low tension battery that kept him murmuring along, he maintained perfect order without ever raising his voice or ruffling a fibre of his mild, flat, efficient being. It made me wonder at that briskness. Where did the life of the children go, in Mr Butcher's classroom? And why did it disappear, so obediently, in Mr Butcher's presence? There was no sign of the sanctions he, surely, held in reserve. Did his simply being so terribly at home in the classroom suggest, to the children, the existence of sanctions that had never to be made visible?

By lunchtime I was deeply depressed. Sitting in a corner of the room, ignored by Mr Butcher with a sort of blank politeness, I had warmed to certain children. There was a boy with bright eyes who, from time to time, seemed to be winking at me. As it happened, he was, except in the matter of his being dressed, uncommonly like a cherub in *The Feast of Venus*. There was another who, under the flat docility of atmosphere, suggested all sorts of interesting wickedness held not very much in reserve.

The afternoon might have been designed as an expedition to opposite poles of teaching. In the first half I saw a man totally at a loss. He dashed at his teaching like someone plunging into a thick and hostile crowd in search of something he had dropped. Driven back by muttering amazement and a chaos of elbows, he stood on the edge of it, his voice on squeaking tiptoe. 'Don't behave like this!' he cried. Then, to me: 'I just don't know what has got into them!' I smiled miserably. Then he was in among them again, making what sounded like wild allegations about the division of fractions. 'Turn the divisor upside down and multiply,' he urged, and the class seethed with noisy puzzlement. 'I've told you this hundreds of times.' Two boys tried to engage me, quite courteously, in conversation. 'What are you doing here, then?' I gave them an awkward smile. 'Interested in football, are you?' I wriggled. 'If you want to see a good game, come up the park on Sundays.' The teacher dashed among us. 'Who's talking, then?' I resisted the temptation to announce my

17

own innocence. 'You are,' said one of the boys, nodding amiably at the teacher. 'You've only got to remember to turn it upside down,' he raved. 'And shut up! Shut up! Turn it upside down and shut up!'

After break I was handed over to a young man with an amused, cool face and very large teeth. 'I like the Socratic method,' he told me. 'Anything can be taught by asking the right questions.' The attentiveness in his room was startling after that other lesson. He was talking about trade unions, but carefully didn't begin by saying so. Instead, he drew from the class such knowledge as they had of social and industrial conditions in the early nineteenth century. Then he shot questions at them that drove them, as it were, to invent for themselves the need for unions. I wondered at it. This was not a method I could use: you wanted a patient, not an excitable head. But how good it was to watch! How eager the boys were to earn his nod, to avoid the comically unhappy face he made when a wrong answer was given, a step missed in the argument! Questions of discipline seemed not to exist when we were all, everyone in the room, trying to locate the forward movement of the argument, trying to keep up with the play of logic.

But how dingy the school was! How dingy the district! When I made my way out through the homegoing school hall, I found myself faced by a noticeboard. It was quartered, and in each quarter were the notices addressed to one of the houses. Clive House, Nelson House, Wellington House, Marlborough House. The headmaster was addressing a hangdog group of boys. 'You know perfectly well that you must bring plimsolls on the days when you have P.T. What's come over you, Grimes? Sapshead? Spriggs?'

Well, names were accidents. All the same, it was curious that the imperial creatures after whom the Green Rise houses were named seemed always to have avoided being called Grimes, or Sapshead, or Spriggs. Spriggs, the victor of Blenheim? Sapshead's Column? Grimes of India?

Boys I'd observed in classrooms dashed past me, their disciplined Green Rise faces suddenly wild and bright with life that Green Rise, I guessed, knew nothing of.

Mince said, beating his gloved hands together: 'A dead waste of time! Oh, what a boring day!'

If this was education, what a sad container it seemed for all that secret young life. I had a vague, unhappy feeling about my day that might have been expressed by saying that certain stale pretensions, called education, had been crowded together most queerly with some of the dowdier facts of our social system . . .

My old schoolfriend Ben said he didn't know how such dreariness was to be endured. Mind you, the government office in which he worked was not a setting that made the heart jump. But it didn't cause the heart horribly to sink, either. The heart remained buoyant, if boringly so, in the Home Office.

What was troubling him at the moment, he said, was the discovery that in marriage you so easily lost sight of the character of your partner. You were too close. As he saw it, marriage could be defined simply as proximity gone mad. He smiled across the room at his wife. 'The dustman probably sees Marie more clearly than I do.' Marie, who was darkly beautiful, made hurriedly the face of someone who wasn't quite sure what a dustman was.

I'd been used since the sixth form to Ben's dry comments on matters that are generally supposed to be romantic ones. When he was dancing attendance on Marie during the war—though casually shuffling attendance might be a truer phrase for it—he'd often amazed me with his detachment. 'What I can't be sure about is what she'll think of my having, as you know, extremely hairy legs. Do you think it will put her off altogether? I wouldn't blame her. Don't you think these things hang very much in the balance and—hairy legs could tilt it the wrong way as easily as anything else?'

I tried to imagine this being said in blank verse. Or how, perhaps, Lovelace might have rhymed another confession of Ben's, when, having asked if I found it easy to tell women they were beautiful (this at a period when in my shyness I'd have found it difficult to tell women the time), he said : 'I've got no further than hinting that I don't have to keep my eyes shut when Marie's around.'

Maybe, I'd sometimes thought, he wasn't giving me a full account of the exchanges between Marie and himself. 'I rather like her, you know, because she runs just like a man. Arms in, you see. *Her knees don't knock!*' On the few occasions during the war when I'd seen them together, Marie had seemed happy in some quite dazzled fashion—not at all like a woman who, perhaps in the middle of a speech in praise of the masculine nature of her knees, had been haltingly assured that she wasn't absolutely hideous.

Anyway, they were married, and had been for three years. 'We're going to see how it turns out,' Ben had written, sternly; the wedding had been in Scotland, where Marie's father was stationed, a Free French officer. Ben still held that it was a strictly experimental arrangement of a fragile kind : which again didn't at all square with Marie's general air, which could be defined as one of extremely reasonable rapture. Such ideas as she might have had herself about the tentative character of their connection were related to Ben's habit of playing rugby football for the Old Boys. 'If I win any glory as a scrum half,' he would say, 'it's snatched away from me by Marie at half-time. She rushes up uttering these little screams and insists on checking my ribs one by one to make sure they're not broken.' 'It's a game for assassins,' was how Marie saw it.

If I was nervous about becoming a teacher, Ben was uneasy about being a civil servant. 'Do you think I might become— irrevocably one? I try to hang on to my proletarian bad manners, but I could easily be corrupted by politer colleagues. What do you say?' 'You know perfectly well,' I said, 'that I've always thought of you as the next Shakespeare but one.' I was six months older than Ben, and we'd always had helpless literary ambitions. Marie laughed and Ben, having looked severe, said : 'I'm lost, you know, in a world of pinstriped men who never make even bad jokes . . .'

He thought he'd not have made a teacher himself. 'I wouldn't have the stamina. I wonder if you have? All those years of it . . . Would you be happy, I wonder? Would you find the opportunities you desire? Always in contact with the undeveloped, always giving a quarter of your mind to things? I'm only thinking aloud, of course . . . and rather insensitively, I guess . . .'

Marie, I understood with a corner of my ear, was thinking aloud for Kate's benefit on an even more alarming theme. I caught the term 'washing machine'.

News of this invention had crossed the Atlantic, and formed part of a vague new vocabulary. Plastics, central heating . . . All related, we thought, to the American way of life at its most enervated and acquisitive. Indolent materialism! I'd been horrified when Ben began to talk about washing machines as if they were not only desirable, but likely of acceptance on the honest British scene. He said: 'I'm hoping to afford to have the odd robot around to make things less boring for Marie. Do you think of doing the same?'

I stared at him helplessly. At school Ben had been an admirer of Diogenes. 'I'm going to live in a tub, you know. Don't you think it's the only thing to do? You can't get a—ugh!—a sideboard or a china cabinet into a tub.' When he was in the Navy he'd been very sharp about the difference between the living space enjoyed by officers and that allotted to the rest, but all the same he seemed to have found in the brutally curtailed quality of naval accommodation a reinforcement of the ideas he'd picked up from the old Greek. Now he was talking of insinuating into this obviously commodious tub an article infinitely more immodest than the flashiest sideboard . . . I reminded him of another enthusiasm of his—for Thoreau's *Walden*. 'Can you imagine Thoreau with a washing machine?'

'Well,' said Ben, sighing. 'That's really not quite the telling reference you think it is. Given, hmm'—I noticed he didn't like to use the actual term—'hmm, mechanical help, he'd have been even freer to roam the woods and so forth.' 'But surely the whole point is that he believed in doing things by hand. He positively enjoyed . . . washing,' I cried. 'I'd like, said Ben, briskly, 'chapter and verse for that.'

Kate and I led them rather nervously down the stairs to the front door of our flat. Mrs Nape, perhaps with her brimming pot, might appear at any moment and eulogise, in her rather mad late-evening way, her son's inches. I caught myself thinking again, absurdly, that Marie should be shielded from such aspects of British life. I had this ridiculous feeling that Britain was always under test, through her French eyes. Well, Ben himself had confessed that he'd been unhappy, watching cinema newsreels by her side during the war, because Winston Churchill was so—fat.

Odd, I thought, all the nervousness that arose in this period of our lives, with old pairs becoming foursomes. 'Marie's fond of Kate, you know,' Ben had said. It was an important bulletin.

I decided to think as little as possible about Ben's astonishing views on washing machines.

The best part of Green Rise turned out to be Old Bandy. He was the woodwork master, with legs that could certainly have done with straightening—perhaps a new mortise and tenon at each knee—and I was not meant to have anything to do with him. Well, I understood fairly enough that I hadn't the appearance of a man handy at craft or much else. But Old Bandy took possession of me one afternoon and insisted that I come with him to his woodwork centre. He had a voice like a crow's, but worse, amazingly ugly, and I was deeply miserable when he brought this strident cackle to bear on the class waiting for him. They were sinful, he seemed to be saying, and needed to be spavined. Somehow I made out that he'd really accused them of being too sensible to stand about talking when marvellous achievements of handicraft were within their grasp. A boy dashed up to him and appeared to say that he was an old idiot and should be tarred and feathered. Old Bandy replied briskly that the boy was a damned bolshie and ought to be clapped in irons. It immediately became evident that they were exchanging amiable and practical comments on the task most of the boys were engaged on : which was to make a stool. Old Bandy addressed the class generally in a vicious spiral of sound, the class smiled with pleasure at finding him in such good temper, and he turned to me. He exhibited his notebooks : full of careful schemes of work. He led me from one piece of boyish carpentry to another : from some excellent piperack ('Monstrous abortion,' he seemed to say, but by now I'd learned to attach no importance at all to what I *thought* he was saying), to a table which it seemed inadequate to call occasional. I also understood that Old Bandy was giving me practical teaching advice. Now and then he'd nudge me in the ribs—it was always at the climax of some long croaking statement—and laugh in his curiously sober fashion. It was laughter glued and screwed and kept for a fortnight in a vice—but pleasant laughter, for all that. Altogether, Old Bandy was one of the nicest men I've ever failed almost entirely to understand. And the instant grasp by him and his boys of whatever was croaked or guffawed by any of them was the best of introductions, because so friendly, to a problem that would,

22

before long, loom quite large. Within Greater London alone, it is easily possible for a native not to understand another native. It was one thing Mr Jepp never got round to discussing; the need we might find ourselves in for an extensive service of interpretation and translation.

5

Back at Isleden, we exchanged astonished accounts of experiences. In Bing's school, a girl possessed by some quite transcendental sense of grievance had run out of the building pursued by a teacher of, Bing said, not abnormal appearance who was crying: 'Don't ever come back here again!' To which the girl had replied: 'Don't worry—I shan't!' It became with us, throughout the course, a kind of refrain. There was a great deal that happened to which a satisfactory response seemed to be: *'Don't worry—I shan't!'* Broom said the oddest thing that happened to him was to fall under the spell of an appallingly bad teacher who chanced to look, though in a damaged way, like the film star Ronald Colman. 'He was awful,' said Broom. 'Behaved hatefully to the children. But then he'd smile and you'd see his ruined *beautiful* teeth under his ruined *beautiful* moustache and . . . I just wanted to cry. Well, I know it was wrong of them to accept me for the course; but they can't have known it was as wrong as *that*! I mean, forgiving a bad teacher because he looked like someone in *Beau Geste*!'

We were back to the exhaustion, among other things, of being among so many strangers. Asked any question about your background, you felt there was no inevitable limit whatever to the answer. Why stop short of any confession? We were always galloping across vast prairies of self-revelation. Bing, for example, told me about his hundred loves. He thought it was probably many fewer than that, but without doing sums it was always the figure that occurred to him. His trouble, he said, was not that he fell out of love, which he never seemed able to do, but that he constantly fell into it. If he could be one of those creatures capable of infinite self-division, all might have been well. He thought Creation had clearly got him confused with such a creature. As it was, his life was a succession of brief felicities and protracted feuds.

No sooner had Bing entrusted me with this confidence than I found the secretary of the dramatic society at my elbow, offering for my inspection the minutes of our first meeting. They were typed impeccably and enclosed in the most virginal folder I ever saw. 'Will you cast your eye over this?' he asked anxiously. He then led me to the main noticeboard, where he'd pinned a permanent frame for our notices: it was made into an open stage by being enclosed within two tiny red curtains, tied back with gold thread. 'I thought something like that—?' he said. I was amazed, quite out of my depth. It was, in my perhaps starved experience of such things, a notice such as might have been made by, oh, a Fabergé among notice-makers. But it turned out to be a fairly commonplace example of the highly competitive notice-making that went on throughout the course.

We were a wildly mixed body of students. Two hundred of us, together for thirteen months: the course punctuated with three teaching practices. We had to choose what was described, in typically muffled language, as an 'emphasis'—between, that is, the junior and the secondary school. This determined some of the lectures we attended, and the dominant nature of school practice. I'd not so much chosen, as rolled dubiously in the direction of, secondary teaching.

In age we ranged from the mid-twenties to the early forties: and we came from a quite extraordinary variety of educational backgrounds. In one direction, for example, there was Arnold: who had charmingly allowed himself to be drafted as producer of *Macbeth*, our chosen play. He was *entirely* charming—a walking smile, and nothing false about it. He seemed to have been almost everything at one time or another—a regular soldier, a teacher of English in France and a teacher of French in England: a clown in a circus: a film actor and a translator of plays. his version of something by Schiller had been heard on the

Third Programme. In the early days of the course he'd been whispered about in the corridors. I'd expected someone tall and physically negligible—on the curious grounds that I could not imagine a dwarfish, plump contributor to the Third Programme. Actually, Arnold was very short and round and, as our first visit to the gym revealed, heavily tattooed. I remember being shocked by the conventional character of the tattooing. There were anchors, hearts and snakes. Any translator of Schiller (this seemed to be my thought) should be tattooed in some original fashion. Arnold was very deeply good-natured—the only person I've ever known who at moments of irritation said what actually sounded like 'Tut tut.'

I never knew what drew Arnold to emergency training. I suspect he had used his talents in small pinches; a little language teaching here, a little acting there, with occasional literary adventures, and at least one attempt to be nobody very much at all, which had taken him into the peacetime Army. Now he was in search of something more solid—though I guessed it might turn out to be no more substantial than the rest. He was one of those people who wander all their lives among the roles for which their gifts qualify them—occupational nomads. For the moment he was giving himself wholeheartedly to the *idea* of being a teacher.

In the other direction there was Rumble, who made the strangest capital out of his feeling of educational deficiency. Rumble's habit was to attach himself to people and begin a process of reducing them. It was a need he had, to discover the strength in a companion and then nibble at it—taking larger bites if opportunity seemed to offer. I noticed it first in his attitude to Bing. 'Of course,' he would say, 'you have a very clear head. Sometimes when I hear you talking I think how muddled I am. People like me are *very* muddled. It was lack of advantage, I suppose. You see, I can only guess at things. Because of my upbringing, without much advantage really, I have to do the best I can by . . . feeling for things. That's it, you see. Getting there by instinct. You have to do that, if you were brought up as I was.' The effect was to suggest that clear-headedness was the helpless failing of the man who'd been overwhelmed with educational advantage. Bing was, in some disgraceful fashion, lucid and knowledgeable : Rumble, exhibiting the triumph of valiant instinct over disadvantage, arrived at knowledge by inspiration.

Bing, who'd not had an easy beginning, and was largely self-taught, would gaze at Rumble, distantly amused. 'We get along somehow, those of us who haven't had much of a chance in life,' Rumble would round it off, exuding satisfaction. I could see that he thought of Bing, at these moments, as a giant felled.

To Arnold he would say: 'You have this way with words. You've never had any trouble with them. I suppose you might even find it difficult to imagine that someone might be awkward with them. If you're awkward with words—as I am, because I lacked advantage—you have a great struggle with them. You have to try hard, all the time, to make words do what you want.' Arnold was, one understood, a facile user of language, to whom words came with spineless promptitude. Words came to Rumble trembling from the shock of their unexpected, improbable capture . . .

There was also, very noisily, in this mixed bag of students, Capper. He would howl, after any lecture whatever: 'It's all bloody rubbish.'

As difficult as in Arnold's case to guess what had drawn Capper to teaching. He was a big man, lumpy in construction: rather as though someone had roughed out, on a fairly grand scale, separate ideas of chest, shoulders, buttocks, legs, and thrown them together, omitting various bridge passages. Capper's head, for example, seemed to turn into a torso on some quite peremptory principle. You expected the apparent absence of connective tissue to show in the shape of creaks and squeaks, as he walked. He entertained one general idea, which was that most of what happened in anything like an official fashion was rot and nonsense, to be growled at and thrust aside. He grumbled about the whole apparatus of things—lectures, notetaking, essay writing. Only one feature of college life gave him pleasure, and that inordinately. He longed to be in the gym. If a period immediately before a gym period showed signs of flowing over the bell—if, perhaps, gentle Salt was making a last few comments on a paper delivered by one of us on Hardy—Capper would sit, clutching gym shoes, grunting his anger. 'Jesus Christ!' he'd cry, in a whisper that in print ought to be rendered in capital letters. 'Bloody hell—what's the idea? Jesus wept!' It seemed impossible

26

that he couldn't be heard by our mild and smiling lecturer. 'So I do think it's difficult to argue, as our good friend Mr Smith had set out to convince us, that Hardy was a man with a happy view of life. It's an interesting argument, but I think we might have to say that it fell down for lack of evidence. Or was pushed over by rather a pressure of evidence the other way.' Gentle Salt, restoring critical balances so brashly overturned. Smith blushing with pleasure at the notion that he'd almost won through with his thesis that Hardy was the poet of good cheer. Capper growling : 'Oh do pack it in ! Oh, why doesn't he shut up?' 'Ah well —I suppose we must bring this to an end.' 'I'd bloody well say so !' 'I'm tempted to add a word or so about Mr Smith's . . . insights into *The Dynasts*.' 'Oh, Jesus !' 'But—next time, perhaps.' Capper up and pushing his way to the door. 'The gym next, I suppose,' Salt would smile, as the door exploded under Capper's shoulders.

And when, after a slow walk through corridors, a thoughtful and reluctant change of dress, I and my fellow inactives found ourselves in the hollow bawling world of the gym, with shouts and the thuds of a football ricocheting from wall to wall, Capper would already have reached the first stage of exhaustion, hurling his huge body through the air that smelt so strongly of bodies less than fresh. I hated the violence of the gym, the bounding and crashing relief with which the actives flung themselves into their play. It reminded me of the gym at school, and of the atmosphere there, so like this one, of rowdy delight in the reprieve from penwork and discussion.

6

'I fancy,' I wrote solemnly in my diary, 'there may be periods of ennui in this course.' A few days later : 'Now that the novelty is wearing off, I suspect possible boredom.' It seemed priggish to feel this. So many students were in such an evident state of excitement. The course delighted them with those very features that were beginning to bore others : the timetables, the making of notes, the lectures—the actually *being* a student. Rumble, always gnawing or nibbling at someone, trying to reduce them to size with his envious teeth, represented in an extreme form an understandable abrasiveness that began to be felt between one kind of student and another.

But it *was* boring. There was James, for example, an extremely agreeable man who took us for practical English, in a muffled, unpractical fashion. I was not greatly in need of his help : but after being exposed to it, found myself strangely . . . in need of help. I was quite clear about the transitive and intransitive character of verbs, until he expounded it. He had gifts that were, so to speak, the reverse of the gifts of the teacher. He was, you could say, a talented obfuscator. 'Mr James will obfuscate English before the morning break twice a week.' More than most of our mentors, he seemed to be caught between one idea—that we were all perhaps geniuses—and another—that we might all very well be idiots. As time went on, he veered, and then ran very fast, towards the latter notion. He seemed also to use up topics sooner than he should. Of most of the items of punctuation, he made one Tuesday a rapid parcel; destroyed our confidence in commas and colons, and never returned to them again. This, as week followed week, forced him into taking us on a quick (but it seemed a very slow) tour of English literature. An example of this was his lecture on Charles Dickens : a writer given, he revealed, to the comic vein. He spent half an hour making sure that this fact about Dickens did not escape us. 'He was a man with a very great sense of humour . . . Ah, five minutes to tea break, I see. But if you were to go very quietly and rather slowly down the stairs . . .'

James, one sensed, felt a mild man's distaste for teaching. Rarely quiet enough for him, never slow enough. He was at the other end of the dynamic scale from Mr Jepp. If Jepp was composed of interesting energies, James was composed of interesting lassitudes.

And then there was Education. That *was* Mr Jepp.

'Each man', read the prospectus, 'will study educational principles'. Each man did so, largely in the main hall first thing in the morning, with Mr Jepp's erratic assistance.

The help he gave us was erratic in that it was sometimes quite horribly riveting, and sometimes sent even the front row to sleep. He'd been a London headmaster, in schools that did not lead a man to cultivate philosophical airiness. With eyes that seemed actually noisy—you felt you could hear them as they performed astounding tricks inside their sockets—and with a moustache that he could, somehow, thrust very far forward, aggressively, so that even at the back of the hall you felt you'd come under some odd hairy attack, he was not the obvious source of information about educational forms of naturalism, or idealism, or pragmatism. And the textbook on which we all leaned was not particularly well matched to him. I sometimes tried to imagine the book that would have given him suitable support : it would, I guess, have had much of the quality of a comic strip. A kind of educational *Beano*. Mr Jepp, at his best, was a man outraged—not by ideas, but by the verbal respectability of the accepted account of ideas. Our textbook was, in that sense, most conventionally dressed. In fact, I used to find myself thinking of all this in terms of Mr Jepp's own clothes. They had clearly started out like those of any other training college lecturer of the time—with some sort of herringbone decency : in his case, a double-breasted decency. But then they'd been inhabited by Mr Jepp. He didn't wear clothes so much as get inside them in order to subject them to outrageous strains from within. Having made a point, for example, he'd raise his arms violently above his head. It might be a very demure point : perhaps, that naturalism in education wouldn't do, and idealism would do, and pragmatism wouldn't do : but if you put them all together, they might just about . . . do. Mr Jepp's arms raised in triumph. The stitches that joined his sleeves to the body of his jacket were more often gaping than not. He did terrible things with buttons, attaching them to extremely remote buttonholes, or simply losing them. His trousers were—again the word is inevitable—*noisily* rumpled. Mr Jepp was a galvanic person, ready to leap across a classroom and nip some act of indiscipline in the nose, ear, or fleshy part of the leg. He was not what you'd immediately think of as an educational theorist.

The lively part of main hall lectures with Mr Jepp came from

29

his quarrel with the task he was given. It was the task of fitting the hurly-burly of education into abstract categories. Talking about Johann Friedrich Herbart, for example, and about Herbart's use of the term *Zucht*, which narrowly means 'discipline' but more widely means 'character-training', Mr Jepp would suddenly become satirical, bringing to bear the more sensational part of his lecturer's equipment. His arms would shoot up, stitches would audibly snap, buttons would fly off : he would tell some terrible story about a monster he'd once taught, whose character was beyond all training—who had, indeed, no character to train. 'Don't forget'—a memorable cry of Mr Jepp's, the whole college leaning forward so as not to miss the snap of a single stitch—'that in Herbart's sense some kids have no character you can train—even you, Smith'—fixing with his terrible eye a student who'd trodden on his toes in some corridor that morning—'even *you* would hunt in vain for a character you could'—his eyes positively gyrating, like those of the dog in *The Tinder Box*—'train!' And all the time you knew that what this was really about was the solemnity—the very existence—of the German language. What Mr Jepp was really saying was—'*Zucht*!—blimey—what a word !'

He was funny, funny, Mr Jepp; and students, in those opening weeks of the course, dined out on his anecdotes. The trouble was that Mr Jepp was also solemn, solemn. If such names as William James, Pestalozzi, Whitehead and Plato could be guaranteed three times out of ten to cause him to behave fascinatingly, they could also be guaranteed seven times out of ten to cause him to behave with appalling dullness. I understood him in this matter. By the same academic respectability that caused his explosions, he was impressed. In fact, he was an intelligent maverick Cockney who felt certain that Plato would have worn a Cambridge scarf, and that Pestalozzi would have spoken with an Oxford accent. He was abashed by their credentials. He was also deeply impressed by their ideas.

I found myself very soon sent to sleep . . . not by those ideas, but by their presentation. I had no capacity to take in a page of prose in which no concrete nouns or vivid verbs appeared. My eye must be able to alight on some word like 'policeman' or 'lamppost', some verb like 'strangled' or 'stroked'. The textbook we used when studying educational principles was stingy with such words. I slid, defeated, unable to find a foothold, down the smooth abstract walls of page after page. At main hall lectures I at first goggled at, and then grew deaf to, Mr Jepp, who was seven times out of ten so much in awe of our textbook, itself so secondhand in its treatment of educational ideas.

All the same, you never knew when Mr Jepp would become fierce or satirical. However diffidently boring his lectures were, it was never sensible to forget that this was much the same lack of sparkle as is manifested by a slumbering volcano. Sudden ferocity was his real forte—unheralded eruptions of furious mischief.

He had amazing eyes, which he could fill with a menacing gleam. They seemed positively to advance, suddenly blazing with light. He made much of 'the teacher's eye'. 'You can pin them to their desks with the right sort of glare,' he told us once, the statement startlingly ill-connected to a previous rambling reference to Plato. 'Learn to rotate 'em! Your eyes are your Number One weapon! Swivel 'em! Stare! Glare!' Illustrating the technique, he had the entire hall cowering. 'Most of you have mild little eyes of which you make no use at all. Become aware of your eyes! Try it! Glare at me, the lot of you! Come on—scare the living daylights out of me!' Hurriedly clambering out of the still gently swinging hammock of educational ideas, three hundred students forced themselves to glower at the platform—an army of embarrassed grimaces. 'Good God!' Jepp cried. 'You wouldn't put the wind up a flock of sheep! Try it at home! Try it on your wives and your grandmothers and your children! You'll be torn to pieces if you go into a classroom with such ladylike eyes!'

He selected the mildest man in the front row. 'Make me blink!' The mildest man did his best . . . his worst. 'I think you *adore* me, *darling!*' Jepp groaned. 'I'm not asking you to melt a lady's heart! You're warning forty desperadoes that you're the master and the skies will fall on them if they so much as move a muscle!' Three hundred students left the hall at the end of that lecture with eyes lowered, cheeks crimson.

He had satirical reservations about methods of teaching that rested on the making of models and other aids. To students all of whom were busy with ingenuities of this sort he would (eyes much advanced) suggest, in no very roundabout way, that they were being duped. 'You stagger into the classroom,' he shouted (he believed also in the teacher's voice, a foghorn), 'with this cardboard creation, it's ten foot by six foot and it's painted in twenty different colours, your wife and you have been working at it for ten weeks, it's cost you half your salary for the whole term, and if you dare let the kids anywhere near it, and if they can understand it when they *do* get near it—which none of them will, because understanding it could qualify you for a Nobel Prize—then what they'll get from it is some earthshaking fact of life such as that if you multiply by 100 you move the decimal point two places to the right.'

Mr Jepp, a comedian scarcely manqué—what professional performer might not have envied him the decades of school platforms that had been the scenes of his triumphant acts!—then demonstrated another feature of the teacher's eye, its capacity most dramatically to lose touch with its companion. He should have lectured in Squinting. 'But,' he said, 'let me warn you. Mock, at your own risk, the visual aid—the model that a whole family could live in, if need be! Mock it at your own risk!' Inadequate now to call the relationship of his eyes a mere squint. 'Make a model exquisite, expensive, a work of art, and totally useless—and you'll pass out of this place an A teacher. Make a model that looks as if you threw it together blindfolded out of any old material you could find in the dustbin, and then kept it under the bed for a couple of years, but that is practical, useful, and within the understanding of the children you teach—and you'll be lucky to get through this course at all.'

This was Mr Jepp at his most anarchic—when you wondered if Mr Trellis, for example, really knew what was going on. It was true that Jepp's attacks on the paramountcy of the visual aid were regarded as strokes of eccentric comedy, with small reference to real life. We were marked for everything we did that could possibly be compared with anything anyone else did : so what more natural than that important marks should be attached to models and constructions of every kind. Still, Mr Jepp's outbursts did amount to very real assaults on the character of the course. They exceeded, surely, the bounds of that contract there appeared to be between him and Mr Trellis, to balance airy idealism with brutal practicality, and vice versa. After all, Mr

Jepp was cutting across all that : he was saying that a certain kind of practicality might itself be airy beyond belief.

My own attitude to all this grew more complex and confused as time went on. The fact is that I had few practical gifts of any kind. I made, with papier mâché, the most laborious puppet in the world, which defied everyone's attempts to nominate a character for it : as a witch, say, a giant, a common soldier, a hunchback. Many suggestions were made, and proved ineffectual. Making patterns with coloured paper was not what I did with a great deal of coloured paper. In marbling with a handmade comb and poster paints I did not achieve what, by the widest sort of definition, is considered to be marbling. And over many miserable weeks I proved to be useless at basket work.

Kate watched as I worked on a wastepaper basket. The term hardly seemed to describe what was taking—oh, not shape : what, in my irritable hands, was taking a shapelessness for which I could only make the wretched claim that it was entirely original. At intervals I placed the thing on a table and went across the room, turning to surprise it. It always surprised me, with its hiccuping outline. I was constantly struggling to prevent it from sealing itself off, losing altogether the surely essential opening at the top.

Damn ! If to be a teacher one must be able to impose one's will on basketwork, papier mâché and bits of coloured adhesive paper, then I was already out of the running.

Most of my companions had what seemed to me a genius for model-making. They produced exquisite graphs, bewitching time charts, vivacious visual aids of all kinds. Farrell, the handicrafts man, treated me with ominous sympathy, laced at times with disbelief. 'Your gift is verbal,' he once said. That was all very well : but since so many of our—ugh!—assessments were given for practical work, I took little heart from this reference to the use of words. Though it did strike me fleetingly that I might test Farrell's sincerity by producing, not an actual wastepaper basket, but a written description of one : ideal, superb, a piece of basketwork that might have stood alongside—oh, the great baskets of all time.

7

Back at the flat, there was Kate. But who was she? Suddenly she seemed as complete a stranger as one could imagine. A great shyness overcame me. How had we arrived at this intimate association? 'You're home, you're home,' she sang. Who was I, this person who was home? What *was* it all about?

Sudden involuntary coldness, even. The loss of marital conviction left us worse than strangers. 'Oh, you don't look pleased to see me. No, don't smile like that. Don't . . .'

It was a false smile. It was the desperate mark of this occasional feeling, that I was unassimilated into the . . . soup of marriage. I was a lump of gristle in the pot. How could one become married, in any convincing fashion : so that this sense of being an unabsorbable ingredient didn't arise, and arise so often at moments when tenderness and conviction were specially called for?

But this *must* be the experience of the newly-married, mustn't it? A good deal of boiling and stirring must be needed before those separate identities began to merge? Could I say that even Ben and Marie yet composed a flawless . . . consommé?

I remembered once trying to ride a tandem. It was with a friend, and we were to go on holiday together on the preposterous machine. Our separate skills as cyclists, put together, didn't produce the skill of tandem-riding. Who was in charge? Two distinct wills at work in matters of steering and balance led again and again to the machine's frightful sideways lurch and crash. We grew angry with each other. 'Well, leave it to me,' he said. 'You take the back saddle and just let me do all the thinking.' I tried to sit, thoughtless, submissive : and some little nervous inclination to prevent a spill, to determine our course, brought us furiously again to the ground.

And then, suddenly, we could do it. We'd hit on the mysterious correct mixture of self-effacement and control. We flashed along, singing, on the machine that was now both of us, a powerful and exhilarating augmentation of solitary cycling.

'I've made you some very special soup,' said Kate in a small voice.

Surely we'd master the machine of marriage, some time . . .?

I was having bad dreams, night after night, about the baby. In one of these the process of gestation was translated into terms of pumping up a bicycle tyre. It was done too energetically and the baby burst. More often I simply dreamed that the baby emerged and was, frankly, not recognisable as one. Because it was mine, it was like one of my mathematical models : I'd forgotten about fingers and toes, I'd put the head in the wrong place. At worst, I'd confused the human shape with the canine. Poor Kate and I were parents of a hit-and-miss sort of dog.

Well, it was awfully like the visual aid we had laboured over, for use in the teaching of fractions. This was done at the behest of Gibling, who lectured in mathematics as if it were a branch of magic. He came into the hall—this is how it seemed to me —and sawed mathematical facts in half, or produced algebraic rabbits out of arithmetical hats. All my old, rather sore memories of totally sober mathematics were scattered. This was maths as a branch of show business. When Kate and I had finished with that visual aid it looked like some hapless attempt to construct a xylophone from cardboard. Kate said : 'I'm sure it would play a tune—if you dared to try it.' As we painted the xylophone in primary colours, we took care not to arouse such music as was in it. One could imagine it—dolorously flabby : a limp and deeply depressing whisper of sound.

And Kate was suddenly consumed with nervous weeping. It had nothing to do with mathematics. It was, I thought forlornly, the result of being converted within less than a year of marriage into a pod, complete with kidney bean. The book we went by had told us, rather earlier, that this audacious creation of ours was that size—a kidney bean's. It was how we'd come to refer to it. My mother had said, recently : 'Daddy and I do wish . . . It's such a funny thing to call it . . .' She had never had much gift for finishing sentences, and this was a subject that made her incomplete as never before. 'Daddy and I would rather you . . . When I was carrying you, we never . . .' I gathered that, enclosed remarkably within my little hesitant mother, I'd never been spoken of. 'We thought,' said mother, oddly, and driving herself to end a sentence, 'it was more natural.'

I'd met Kate when she joined the amateur dramatic society of which I was a groaning member. Well, groaning because it took so much time, it seized you and absorbed you utterly: which was bad enough if you had a sizeable role, something to work at: worse when it was a matter of filling in along the decorative margins of some rubbishy piece written specially for amateurs . . . But Alec, our producer, was not easily resisted when it came to casting: or to the fact, which he could express most poignantly, that amateur actresses were ten a penny, and amateur actors had to be mined for. So I was always, petulantly, enchantedly, submitting to the notion that I should represent some extremely minor character, in order to permit Alec himself to play some extremely major one.

I was tremendously disposed to be married. This had, I hoped, nothing to do with Ben having so amazingly got himself coupled with Marie. Or did it have nothing to do with that? It was certainly awkward, being three in number. I had thought that my being Ben's closest friend might wholly endear me to Marie. In fact, it seemed to expose me to severe and often dissatisfied scrutiny. She thought I saw Ben too seldom: or imposed myself upon him too often. I was not there when he was in need of stimulation, and *was* there when he was in need of relaxation. 'I'm sorry Marie's a bit sharp at times,' said Ben. 'She likes you, you know.' (Another important bulletin.) 'The trouble is, she thinks I'm a nitwit who needs protecting. Left to myself, I'd allow my friends to trample all over me.' It was *very* awkward, being three. And I did, anyway, in an absolute fashion, desire to be married. It was an effect, I believed, not only of a sanguine nature, but also of childhood reading. I had always been in love with the idea of love. Not quite a fool, I hoped, I was still very much in favour of living happily ever after.

In my dreams, before I met Kate, I was always finding myself being mismarried.

I married my sister (who said, glaring round the larder in our earliest home, where the reception was taking place: 'It's just the kind of thing we all expected you to do'). I married a young woman without a face, or rather with a face that the dream kept attempting, without success, to patch together from standard-shaped noses and blank chins. I married a total stranger with a piercing cackle and (inexplicably) grubby legs, on which the dream focussed at length. I married a young woman on the top of a bus who clipped tickets ill-temperedly while I covered her with dejected kisses. I married my friend Roger Bunce's mother, who said she looked forward to teaching me to knit. 'You have condemned yourself to a lifetime of needlework,' the officiating parson laughed: walking away only to wheel and declare, bitingly: 'I am H. G. Wells!' It was to the desolate sense of being wrongly married that, on too many mornings, I woke. You'd have thought, given such anxiety in the matter, that I was under siege from unsuitable lovers. But it wasn't so. My sense of being menaced was matched only by my total lack of amorous enemies.

Until, that is, Kate appeared. I thought she was disqualified from the start by being so obviously a nice person. She was honest; anxious to be of help to people; good-humoured and, as an actress, an excellent comedian. These were not the stormy and mysterious qualities of a lover, as I understood the science of it. One could adore, surely, only what was terribly and teasingly difficult of access. A splendid sort of dishonesty, in fact : and the very reverse of busy helpfulness: and a tendency to glamorous ill-humour. As for acting, the lady would clearly be a tragedian. I felt safe in respect of Kate. That's to say, I felt about her as about any agreeable friend.

And then, suddenly, I didn't.

We were coming back in a bus from a festival performance of Chehov's *The Proposal*. It was one of Kate's best roles—that of the spinster whose last hope of marriage lay in the tremulous intentions of a neighbour, a hypochondriac. The scene of his proposal turns from simpering goodwill to noisy animosity when he and her father begin to make claims and counterclaims for their various dogs. The discovery that they don't agree about dogs reminds them that they don't agree about anything. There's nothing left for the girl but to bring her father to his senses with a powerful display of hysterics.

I must say that Kate lying back in a chair, her legs stuck

37

out like a Dutch doll's with fury—Kate, hammering with her heels on the floor—Kate, tearing asunder the careful tower of her Russian spinster's hair : all that ran oddly counter to the notion of Kate as an honest and pleasant female friend. I was the prompter on this occasion, and found myself staring from the wings at Kate's make-up, which was quite fiercely white, with dots of rouge on her cheek, to suggest the plain spinster. This make-up suddenly amounted to a reminder that Kate wasn't remotely plain. I began to feel enormously jealous of Ivan Vassilyevich Lomov, the suitor in the case.

On the bus coming home, I may have felt extremely tired—or it may have been that some subliminal maker of scenarios inside me had seen where a sensation of extreme tiredness might lead. It led to my heeling over very suddenly and ending up—my head ending up—on Kate's shoulder. She made no complaint about this, but continued with what she'd been saying : something about the performance by our nearest rivals. When the internal scenarist arranged for my head to slip further, on to her bosom, she did not come to a halt. I became amazingly aware of the existence of Kate's heart. It was like having one's ear to the door, if it has a door, of a ship's engine room. I had never before listened so closely to anyone's heart. It seemed to me that the unstartled flow of Kate's chatter was at variance with her heartbeat. Her heart was hurrying, with hesitant and irregular steps, along some . . . path? It stopped now and then to listen, to look nervously round, before hurrying on. I thought I should mention this to Kate, as an alarming departure from what one understood was the proper behaviour of a heart, but discovered that she was stroking my hair. For some reason this action demanded my full attention, and in giving it I fell asleep.

And when I woke up, it was to months of what, in retrospect, I think of as having some stupendously difficult suit fitted, by some stupendously clumsy tailor.

There was this long period when every failure in cut and measurement made itself felt. Times, indeed, when we appeared perfectly made for each other, seam to seam. Then all was tenderness, and those marvellous aching jokes that courtship breeds, beautiful teasings. Moments of that whole contentment that otherwise we know only as children, when the heart is singing, no fraction of it silent, and all is well. *All* is well. Opposite

38

Kate's house, ten minutes walk from my own, there was a pillar-box : it was overlooked by the window of her parents' bedroom : night after night, oh deep into night after night, we'd prop our totally exhausted chins on our totally exhausted folded arms on top of the pillar box, and exchange hot kisses—how very simply *hot* you become, courting, a feverish failure of the thermostat !— and I'd make jokes about Kate's father and the possibility of his opening fire, until we could almost see him leaning out of the window, levelling something like a blunderbuss. And sometimes, moved by a wry panic, a great dread of making any choice at all out of what seemed an infinite background of choice, I'd make cruel jokes about blunderbusses. Buss was the old word for kiss, wasn't it, and our kisses were blunderbusses, it was all wrong . . .

The horizon was still immensely distant, and I did not want to bring it close . . . And then I *did* want to bring it close, I shuddered with horror at the thought of such thrilling space, I wanted the restrictions of love, and for it to have a name, and I wanted the name to be Kate . . .

And so, torn between submission and rebellion, I subjected her to the most outrageous vacillations of feeling. And she responded with steadiness and gravity of love. I would find this desire in me, for a life of one's own, sharply defined in terms of having a wife, and a place to live. I would love Kate, no hesitation in it, her skin so smooth, her eyes so big and solemn : and there'd be a week of such a wish, followed by a week of despairing doubt, when I'd wonder how you distinguished the real value of anything from the fabrications of desire and longing.

And at times it would seem to me incredible that one could be so fastidious : about such delights, so uncertain.

Then there came a decisive night. It had been an immensely hot day, one of those very great summer days : and even after midnight, the world seemed still to have its shirtsleeves rolled up, its blouse unbuttoned. The warmth somehow had become a part of the stillness of things, though the stillness itself had a sort of electric languor about it, a tension between the inert and the explosive that scarcely made it stillness at all. It was a vibrant stillness. We came to a halt somewhere in the middle of a field, quite early in the evening. Time did not pass : we were enclosed in deepening dusk, as if we were in the process of being preserved : and then the moon came, and we were enclosed

39

instead in a silver radiance that grew more and more intense. It laid shadows under the trees as black as licorice. A pond in a dip beyond us was a flash of steel. It seemed extraordinary, to be illuminated there, at the heart of a long shallow valley, surrounded by suburbs, and to be so free, to make silver love, to murmur and laugh and grow enormously sleepy and then, again, enormously wakeful. It was indeed, and I look back and see it was, a night when we were welded together by some magical sort of engineering.

And when we walked home, alone awake of all the world, the hedges chattered drily: a straw stack whispered from corner to corner: and the stillness had become complete, so that the beauty of a full standing tree in the moonlight lay not so much in the tree as in its perfect lack of all movement. Then we were back among houses, and from open windows came the heavy breath of sleepers.

And when I asked Kate to marry me, there was suddenly a head framed in a window, and a voice cried: *'Will you buggers shut up and go away!'*

And we went away and got married . . .

8

The days at Isleden quickly became repetitive. We spent much time in activities I'd never had much gift for. Nature study, for instance. We were always sketching leaves, and I was always struggling to remember one leaf from the next.

My renderings of leaves, and even more of worms, caused me deep shame. To me it seemed that our group bristled with Dürers, with a few Leonardo da Vincis bringing up the rear. There was also a student called Radwell who turned his drawings into charming fantasies, of an *art nouveau* kind. *His* worms were plainly enchanted princes—waiting, perhaps, for kisses from his snails, who were enchanted princesses. *My* worms had the character of ill-made lead pencils. They had never lived.

And once more I failed to keep in mind the distinction between petals and sepals and stamens. I failed to understand the chain of life. Or rather, I understood it for a day or two—dined out on it—astounded Kate with it. And then it had gone. It was the everlasting character of my mind. My mind was *erasive*.

It had been indicated, but without enthusiasm, that those who could not subscribe to Religious Instruction—having thought the matter over and done their best to deal with this weakness in themselves—might meet with the principal on Friday mornings, when the rest of the college were learning how to insinuate into the classroom a fairly bland version of Christianity.

There were a dozen of us, as it turned out. I sat, the first morning, between Broom and Bing, opposite Mr Trellis : who smiled at us with sad sweetness, and then for a long time was silent. There was some impression that we were being prayed for. 'Well, then,' he said at last. 'Perhaps I might most usefully begin with a survey of man's attempts to explain his existence on Earth.' A student called Trimmer, large and uneasy, laughed at this. 'If that would suit you, Mr Trimmer,' said the principal, pleasantly. 'Oh yes,' said Trimmer. 'Carry on. I was only laughing.' When Mr Trellis smiled at him, at an even deeper level of sorrow, Trimmer became very agitated. 'I just . . . laughed,' he said. 'I don't know why I laughed, really.' 'Well, let me make a start . . .' said Mr Trellis : but did not do so for another long moment, as if he expected further outbreaks of mere laughter, inexplicable to those responsible for it.

Then, in his low voice, which seemed to be addressed to some other audience situated somewhere within his own frame, he talked for half an hour—indeed, until the session was over. The Babylonians . . . the Greeks . . . the Romans . . . Mohammedanism . . . Catholics and Protestants . . . He came to Science. Perhaps Science was simply another faith, that left as many mysteries as its rivals. If, indeed, Science *was* the rival of Religion . . . If nothing more was to be learned from Science, as to causes and origins, then perhaps, some would argue, one

41

might as well cling to beliefs that could muster, after all, an impressive band of adherents.

In later sessions, the principal adopted what we thought of as another tactic. No one was sure that it was fair to think of him as a tactician, intent on driving us back to the fold. But he certainly succeeded in keeping the occasion slow, low, oddly drab and clumsy. He mainly did it by addressing himself to Trimmer. Or rather, Trimmer was the sort of person who, if a ball were thrown into the air, would feel bound to rush about in the attempt to catch it, however much it might be beyond his reach. And Mr Trellis seemed to be feeding this habit of his. So he would offer us a piece of philosophical fielding practice—would loft at us some question that none but Trimmer would leap for except after irritated thought. 'What do you make, then, of the Pauline view of things?' Given a moment to recover, one of us might have asked : 'What exactly would you say *is* the Pauline view of things?' But Trimmer would rush forward at once. His general approach was that anyone who put a question of the smallest complexity, to himself or to others, was inflicting unnecessary pain and worry. So his constant cry was : 'Does it matter?' But it was less a cry than a sheepish mumble. 'Where does this get us? . . . How does that help?' 'You must have given some thought to St Paul, Mr Trimmer.' 'Well, I haven't bothered much. He believed . . . well, when you think what he believed!' 'What special beliefs of his, Mr Trimmer?' 'Well, they all had different ones, didn't they? I mean, that was why there were all those religious wars.' 'Wait a minute, Mr Trimmer.' The principal's face filled with sweet indulgence—with just a hint of triumph. 'I think you're unwise to rush from one idea to another so very fast. I think I'd better say something about St Paul.' Another long, slow, low monologue—this time very definitely addressed to a body of students seated inside his stomach. Then the college bell. 'Well, gentlemen—those of you who are still interested—next Friday.'

'No doubt about it,' said Bing. 'His aim is to bore us back into the Faith.'

Dr Moss came in part-time to lecture on psychology. He approached this subject with, as it struck us, a surprising unwillingness to set much store by it at all. In talking of Freud he seemed always to be on the edge of laughing Freud out of court. 'Well, what Freud argues . . .' he used to say, as if the very phrase was enough to clinch the contrary opinion. Jung he treated with such respect as verged on total disrespect. ('Jung, you will not be surprised to hear, did not agree with anyone else on this topic . . .') Dr Moss was always ready, in full public view, to scamper out of the reach of these great men, and into the embrace of what he called commonsense. 'After all, gentlemen, commonsense tells us . . .' He had a blunt mind, and I used to wonder about the thesis that had gained him his doctorate. *A Study of Some Bluff Realities in the Field of Educational Psychology?* 'My goodness, we all know about little children,' he would cry, suddenly maddened by some insight he was required to report from the work of Professor Piaget, who had simply spent a lifetime meticulously observing the very young. 'Give some sound fellow a couple of days with Class 1A and he will . . .'—here Dr Moss was inclined to throw his lecture notes disparagingly to one side—'. . . he will know a deuce of a lot of useful things about the little tiddlers.'

One of the gulfs between Dr Freud and Dr Moss, one saw, lay in the latter's use of phrases like 'little tiddlers' or 'little chaps'. Such phrases are not common in the work of the great Viennese. The truth was that Dr Moss represented English empiricism at its most apoplectic. Any kind of intellectual elaboration seemed to him the mark of the devious, tragically over-brainy intellectual. He wanted to save us from it. And one has to say that very few serious obstacles were placed in his way.

There were these great elements in the course, philosophy and psychology, and it was interesting to observe how they were laid low. Essentially they were foreign products and they were dealt with accordingly in many a lecture. Any alien eye Dr Moss left unblacked, Mr Jepp would set out to injure in some boisterous assault on the whole notion of things ever being theoretical or philosophically tentative.

True that Mr Jepp was in awe of the philosophers and theorists. Yet with him, as with others among our instructors, the tug-of-war at the heart of teacher training, between abstract ideas and only too concrete realities, found him again and again sneaking across to add his weight to the solid rather than the cerebral side. It was the same with Dr Moss. As an old teacher, trained to analyse behaviour, he was marvellous on such things as the use of the voice in the classroom. Mr Jepp was inclined to give the impression that a teacher's voice was at its best when raised. This was because his own voice was barely capable of being lowered. Had there ever been some means of reducing its volume, it had long since been lost. In fact, Mr Jepp secured vital variations by qualities of huskiness, and half a dozen different kinds of gratingness, that no ordinary voice could manage. Dr Moss merely pointed out, again and again, with anecdotal embellishments, the truth that the noise level in a classroom was established, certain rudimentary problems of discipline having been solved, by the teacher. Roughly speaking, the quiet teacher had a quiet class, and the noisy teacher had a noisy one. His bluffness and bluntness suddenly valuable, Dr Moss on such topics was not easily forgotten . . .

But still there were those outlandish ingredients of the course to be disposed of, without obvious disrespect : the intellectual elements. There was one great means of dealing with them. It was to treat of them as dully as possible.

On the basis of an immensely dull textbook, Mr Jepp was dull about a great range of figures, from Aristotle onwards. Mr Trellis, in a special lecture, was quite spectacularly, almost thrillingly dull about Locke. Dr Moss, once he'd stopped talking about classroom realities, was simply dull about everything and everybody, much of the time. Lectures on the philosophy and aims of education, and on the findings of psychology as they impinged upon education, caused among us a tedium—before and during and after—that I remember even now with pain.

'My God, this course is boring,' my diary had taken to groaning.

The devil of it was, I now think, that though we were being trained for work in which ideas were rather plainly of importance, we were being subjected to a sort of aversion therapy in the matter of having ideas, of any kind. If the intention had been to make ideas nauseous to us, it could not have been better pursued. The essential philistinism of our training was enabled to run riot. Mention idealism, the ego and the id, pragmatism, nature and nurture, behaviourism, environment, Johann Friedrich Herbart, Plato, Maria Montessori . . . oh, mention any such thing or person within the walls of Isleden, and you would have made, by

44

that mere mention, an excellent joke, and there would be a great deal of appreciative falling about, and clutching of aching ribs.

If ideas retained any value at all, it was because a student here and there had some, and felt strongly about them, and accordingly roused strong feelings in those who chanced to have contrary ideas. It was quite absurd, I think, looking back. Officially ideas were being damped out of existence, by an elaborate and expensive system of lectures and text books; unofficially, they were inclined to be explosive and—my goodness, yes—fairly educative.

There was the day when, in one of our non-religious seminars, I found myself espousing the idea that there might be some sort of fixed *good* in the pattern of things.

Socially, let alone philosophically, it was one of those sickening moments when at 12.15, say, you are in favour, rather liked, quite popular, indeed, and at 12.16 you are in total and shattering disgrace. We were talking about the term, 'a good life': and Mr Jepp, who was in the chair that week, invited us to look at the word 'good': which we did harmlessly until this need of philosophical affirmation seized me, and I stated that there was in the world a permanent essence for which the word was 'good'. Man was born, I rushed on to say, with the equipment with which he could detect this essence. Bing was sitting next to me, and I felt his horror as a positive shudder. Broom, several places away, actually cried out.

Mr Jepp, his moustache seeming to have joined forces with his eyebrows, invited me to repeat my assertion. I did so, and at once saw that I did not really believe this: and that, if I did, I should have been with the majority, doing R.I. Too late! My education on this issue had taken, I should guess, somewhere in the region of one or two minutes: fairly rapid. But I should, it was obvious, have thought it out years before. My two friends discussed the matter at great length, once the seminar was over. They talked of it as if I were not there, as if they were talking in the neighbourhood, say, of the ruins of London, blown up by some outrageous bomb. How could this otherwise acceptable associate of theirs have this daft worm at his heart?

'I've always thought,' said Broom, 'that there was something bourgeois about him—a sort of aristocratic elegance, in fact . . . What do you say, Bing?'

45

'At least one cog in the machine meshes only with elitist notions,' said Bing.

I was, alongside my sense of disgrace, rather flattered. Yes, yes, I found I was quite pleased to be thought of as one struggling against bourgeois, possibly even aristocratic, tendencies.

9

Over the dull days, a spectacular sky above the flattest of landscapes, hung the words of *Macbeth*, the play we'd chosen to perform. Macbeth was being played by a student called Rayner, who seemed always, curiously, to be wearing a porkpie hat set at a slant. He wasn't really doing so; he wasn't wearing a hat at all. But his performance had about it some quality as of . . . commercial travelling. Somehow, as we returned from the battle in the first scene—I was playing Banquo—I felt we were on our way home from a sales trip in the further Highlands. The witches were . . . dissatisfied customers? Macbeth trafficked in women's garb and, appearing in their rags, the witches were protesting against the rubbish he sold them.

I don't mean that I thought things out in this fashion. It was on the edge of my mind that the drama had this curiously hucksterish nature. It all arose, I guess, from Rayner's own character, which proved stronger than the one offered to him by Shakespeare. Rayner in fact was a salesman, not of women's clothing, but of bright ideas and dazzling notions. He was a leader of a group of students who could do nothing quietly or modestly. Giving a lesson during teaching practice on Australia, and wishing to make some point about the Mediterranean character of some areas of that continent, Rayner entered the classroom like a sort of pedagogic Nell Gwyn : that is, he carried a basket of oranges, which he distributed by flinging one, more or less accurately, at each member of the class. The connection between the south coastal region of Australia and oranges was fixed for ever in the minds of all those present; though Broom thought it might with some have brought about a traumatic association, the effects of which were difficult to imagine, between being taught by a student and being rather dangerously bombarded with fruit. Bing thought Rayner lucky not to have been taking a lesson on fishing in Russian waters: thirty-five packets of caviare would have represented an even greater strain on his pocket. Not, as Broom commented, that one had any doubt that Rayner would have supplied the caviare. One felt he always knew ways of achieving whatever a plain simple student would regard as impossibly expensive or insensately impractical.

It was much the same with Perring, an ex-policeman who played Duncan. That is, *he* had indelibly the habits of his previous occupation; and the pious regality of Duncan, as embodied by Shakespeare, had no weight against Perring's own sturdy settledness of character.

This castle has a pleasant seat

says Duncan, fatally entering the home of the Macbeths,

the air
Nimbly and sweetly recommends itself
Unto our gentle senses.

It was straight out of Perring's policeman's notebook, and boded ill for the castle, on which he had been keeping observation for some time, his suspicions almost certainly aroused by the very temple-haunting martlets of which, so enchantingly, Banquo went on to speak. Uttering Banquo's lines, with their sunshiny phrases—'this guest of summer'—'the heaven's breath smells wooingly here'—I'd feel I was speaking the words of the most delightful holiday brochure ever written. But Perring's eye would be fixed on me with total sternness, and one felt there was small hope for the martlet. Charged with haunting. Alternatively with making his pendent bed and procreant cradle on assorted jutties, friezes, buttresses and coigns of vantage. 'I followed this martlet . . .'

Miss Longbone, who lectured on science, was cast as Lady

Macbeth. Though the word 'cast' is too energetic. Rather she was gently dropped into place as the tyrant's terrible lady. Her qualifications for the role were not obvious ones. She had a voice adjusted in scale and dynamics to the sixth form rooms of girls' grammar schools. She stood with legs sensibly together : her hands meeting in front of her, palms up to support an invisible textbook. This was positively her only public posture. One could not imagine the disguise that would cast even the shadow of a doubt on her natural modesty and unassertiveness.

'Come to my woman's breasts,' she murmured—it was, one felt, a late afternoon lesson, and the class was being given this instruction straight out of her lesson notes—'and take my milk for gall.' Arnold said : 'Oh God ! You're in a bit of a passion here, Miss Longbone. Can you sound as though you mean it ?' Miss Longbone smiled unhappily. She raised her voice by a fine fraction of a decibel—seemed to be tossing her phantom textbook into the air and catching it again. 'You murdering ministers,' she mildly categorised her class of clever girls. *'Murdering!'* Arnold howled. 'Oh dear,' said Miss Longbone.

Arnold himself, though Miss Longbone's dabs at murderousness made him mad, was too gentle to be a good producer. Or too inclined to be knocked sideways if there was any riposte to some direction he gave. 'Really,' he told Perring, 'you are a devout old man, as well as a king, and fatally trusting. Can't feel, you know, that *you* would ever get down on your knees. Duncan talks about his gentle senses. All your senses are fierce ones.' 'My goodness,' Perring said, dismayed, with a glance down at his invisible policeman's notebook. 'Oh dear. I don't feel it like that at all, you know. He *is* the king, you know.' 'Oh good Lord, I'm aware of that,' Arnold groaned, clutching his brow. 'How can I put it ? How can I convince you ?' To groans he would add moans : he would assault himself in various parts of the body with the flat of a hand. 'I don't see how you can't see it !' Then he would collapse into one of his rather splendid smiles. Arnold was a subtle man, with a good and busy mind, but the collision of human beings discommoded him, he'd been created with absolutely no powers of persuasion. His maker, however, had been good enough to provide him with this smile, which signalled his submission to his own impotence. Everyone liked Arnold. But for all his sensitive understanding of Shakespeare,

48

he was the worst imaginable of producers for a gaggle of amateur actors. Faced, amazed, with Rayner's tendency to play Macbeth as a lethally-minded salesman, Perring's view of Duncan as a policeman enthroned, and Miss Longbone's approach to Lady Macbeth as an introverted sixth form teacher, Arnold raged, stuttered, was eloquent—and then took refuge in his brilliant smile.

10

The first teaching practice was approaching, and advice accumulated.

It was Mr Gould, Science, who warned us not to agree to stay behind in a classroom with a female pupil, unchaperoned. He also told us about a girl he'd taught himself who'd done something extremely improbable with a test-tube. The moral was a little uncertain : but it seemed to be that in mixed classes one should think twice before using any form of scientific glassware.

Dr Moss said that if we promised to kill a lad on the repetition of an offence, and the offence was repeated, the lad must be killed. To generalise, all aimless threats were to be avoided. It was good advice : but rather like telling a non-swimmer that, finding himself out of his depth, he should on no account allow himself to sink. Face to face with awkward children, we all found that we threatened death : and our threats always met with defiance : and on every occasion we excluded murder from the possible responses.

All this prefatory work, these admonitions and so on, marked by good sense, certainly, had the mark also of absurd and abstract irrelevance. It was like, through lectures and other kinds of verbal instruction, trying to learn to ride a bike. And this was true of the lesson notes we were required to practise.

It was the oddest exercise : perhaps rather more like attempting to plan one's first love affair in the total absence not only of amorous experience but also of a beloved. First you must set out the aim of the lesson. The idea was plausible enough : you must cultivate the habit of knowing precisely what you were doing. But the background was one of very precisely not knowing what you might be able to do. A poetry lesson with a B stream, mixed class, second year. Length of lesson : thirty-five minutes. What intentions would it be sensible to have? Enormous possibilities would float into my mind, and then be hurriedly bundled out of it. 'To inculcate an understanding of the ballad.' Oh, clearly too huge ! I remembered one of my wilder early lessons at the prep school : an occasion when it had not struck me as unpractical to cover, in half an hour, the entire history of Roman London. Panic-stricken, I would rush to the other extreme : the envisaging of a lesson of a drastically shrunken kind. Aim : 'To read and discuss the first stanzas of *Sir Patrick Spens*—'

Then I would struggle uneasily to *see*, in my planner's inward eye, those thirty-five boys and girls. Unimaginable, when it came to it, they nevertheless hurled themselves between me and my ideal aims. We were advised to bear in mind the practicalities of the classroom. Though it might seem no part of this wistful and elegant exercise, one must consider, for example, the giving out of materials. I knew a little about this. The distribution of thirty-five copies of *Sir Patrick Spens*—the selection, simply, of a hoaxproof method of transferring those copies from my custody to that of my thirty-five phantoms—could well become a dominant feature, if not the substance, of the lesson. 'Aim of lesson : to give out copies of the ballad.' I knew that I was peculiarly susceptible to an excess of monitors, childish aides. I was easy game for anyone who'd say (or bellow, or sing) : 'Sir, let me do it—.' I'd always been weak on distribution. But how to apply my uneasy experience to this lesson on *Sir Patrick Spens*? It was possibly quite inapposite experience, too, since I couldn't tell how like my fourteen or so prep school boys thirty-five mixed B-streamers might turn out to be. In a carefully ruled margin, a time had to be given for each phase of the lesson. 'Distribution of copies of the ballad : Thirty minutes'? This was not impossibly a realistic guess at the time involved. But if I wrote that, I'd be clearly inviting an accusation of pessimism, if not of defeatism. I'd clap my telescope, then, to my blind eye, and note : 'Distribution : two minutes.' Then I'd sit gazing at my watch as two minutes ticked away. My God—it was eternity! Now very uneasy indeed, I'd reach a final figure : 'Distribution : one minute.' Hmm!

We were sent on preliminary visits to our first practice schools. Mine was a junior boys' school, somewhere in an old tangle of streets in North London. It was, I found, a gaunt, grey district : the school easy to spot, towering above little houses. I walked round it, nervously curious. Nothing about it seemed designed to please. Its name was carved on a wall in stone that had turned unpleasantly brown : Eastbourne Road School, it said in lettering half-heartedly decorative, 1899. There were lots of little arched entrances each with its iron gate. At last I forced myself to go in. Gloomy stone staircases : a big hall, surrounded by classrooms that somehow had the appearance of huge crates.

'I've only just come myself,' said the headmaster, looking round a narrow room bursting with cupboards and files. 'I mean to make some changes.'

'Yes,' I said wretchedly. A kindly and helpful man, the Head had quickly made up a timetable for my month's visit. But I felt deeply dejected. The place smelt so stale : even the Head's new broom briskness seemed rather terrible, as though a creature of merely normal capacities should have stood boasting in the Augean stables. Suddenly, Isleden seemed very distant—all those lectures and notes and grand assertions, quite unconnected with this hollow building, which squeaked, groaned, squealed, sighed.

There was a tap on the door. In came a grimy boy of, perhaps, eleven, pushing in front of him two even grimier smaller boys. All three faces were sadly slack.

'What's this?' asked the Head.

'Bawling,' said the bigger boy.

'Where?'

'Bawling. Out there.' He gestured vaguely through the door with a black thumb.

'Bigger lad's a prefect. System started by my predecessor,' the headmaster muttered. 'I'm stopping it. These fellows aren't fit for authority.'

The unfitness seemed to be demonstrated by the violently red ear of one of the smaller boys.

'Well,' said the Head, 'what have you to say?'

"E give me a clip on the ear'ole,' said the boy. His trousers were some adult's, cut down, and little seat left in them.

'On the *ear*,' said the headmaster. 'Who hit you on the ear?'

'The bloke what bunged us in 'ere.'

The rest of their defence I was unable to follow. These little children seemed able to speak with their mouths closed. I thought wistfully of Old Bandy at Green Rise—by comparison, a champion elocutionist.

My depression deeper, I went on a tour of the classrooms. How dreary they were, so large, so grubbily naked, lit by gas: old curling pictures on the walls. In some rooms the desks were set on steps. Awful double desks.

One of the masters—kindly but fearsome of face, huge nose and rotting teeth. 'What lesson shall I take with your class?'

'Take geography. Argentine. Meat.' He turned away. 'You'll find they can't read or write.'

'And arithmetic?'

He tapped a dilapidated blackboard, covered with examples of the addition of £ *s. d.* 'Try this. Some can do it—lots can't.'

In the lowest class, a youngish man with strained eyes. He was collecting books: the room rang with sound. 'You being here— they're noisy.' Distractedly he showed me a history book, but his explanations, desperate ones, were interlarded with wild roars— 'Hands on heads!'—and sudden dartings. Face purple, he would bend down to some little offender—chosen at random, so far as I could see—and bellow: 'I didn't tell you to do that, did I? You're daft, aren't you?' Then he would shake the child until his legs were skidding about the floor, bang away at the boy's bottom and return to me. It was a nightmare; the *worst* of it being that he seemed to have lost any idea of how grotesque and hideous this must appear to an outsider.

I came away astonished, with the queerest picture in my mind of all those wretched little boys sitting in their utterly obsolete school. 'Their primary need,' I found myself thinking, 'is not education, but decent surroundings.'

11

I didn't mention to Kate the sadness this caused me. And in any case—there was a holiday first. Isleden rushed out into the summer that had been burning, teasingly, round the college ever since we arrived. Arnold went to some eyrie in the Pyrenees, and we wondered if he would remember to return. Mr Jepp announced that he'd be instructing various beds of roses in floricultural principles. Jack Hagger, the tremendously gentle admirer of Joseph Stalin who ran the Socialist Society, was off to Hungary, his eyes already expectant of Utopia.

And Kate caught sight of an advertisement in the *New Statesman*: made a phone call: and bore me off in a train to Cornwall. It was one of the unmistakable advantages of marriage: being so decisively managed for such splendid ends. Though, in the world I came from, taking a holiday on impulse was of the same moral order as bigamy or nudism. I was delighted and horrified.

Nothing like the east coast I'd always known. In a wrinkle of cliff overlooking more sea than I'd ever observed before in one spot, a cottage, long and white, its roof in the sun a green sort of silver. Mrs Dorf was a Scandinavian bishop's daughter: wintered as an actress in London: spent the summer with her two small children in Little Perran. She was explosively unlike any of the seaside landladies of my respectable childhood. On the first evening she shouted details of her autobiography through a lavatory door at Kate, within. 'Do you think me too informal?' she paused to ask me. I responded with what I hoped was the smile of a man enormously opposed to regarding lavatory doors as any bar to conversation.

We walked next day to the famous nearby village. The houses climbed on each other's shoulders out of the narrow cleft of the harbour. Compared with what was to come within ten years, the sense the place had of itself as a holiday resort was still simple and innocent. We sat for a long time on the highest beak of the cliff, to one side of the village, staring at the wrinkling immensity of water: feeling utterly at peace inside the harsh tent of sound made by gulls . . .

Mrs Dorf saw that I was reading A. S. Neill, and said she much admired him. However, her own children were hooligans, as we must have noticed, and she wondered if Neill might be slightly to blame: that is in having persuaded her, through his books, against severities. I said, in a shyly muffled fashion, that I thought that if A. S. Neill had not existed, she would have invented him. I said little about the children, not being sure what to say. Kate adored them, for their sturdiness and their brown limbs and their comical candour. I liked all that, but with professional nervousness had observed that I did not know what to do when little Nikki, aged seven, boxed my ears, or dug his nails into my neck. I could not discern the moment—the split second, it might be—when sympathy for young vigour might justly turn into rejection of young violence. I did not really suppose that on my next teaching practice I would suffer from such direct assaults on ears or neck, but still I had an uneasy feeling that my uncertainty in respect of Nikki might be a harbinger of vaster uncertainties in respect of—oh God, perhaps forty years of children to come?

Ah, the view from the garden of Little Perran Cottage! There were the great green cliffs folding together, and the marvellous amplitude of sea: it glittered under the sun like a blue pavement under golden rainfall. And always, making every day some sort of sadly jolly Sunday, the tolling of a bell-buoy. Every wave a bell-ringer.

Humped round the village there were armchairs of cliff to sit in. We could not imagine how we would ever return to London. The days came one after another huge with sun: the sun burned us all into the scene. Every nick in the rock had its coloured bather. The glittering could be detected, across miles of sea, of every little wave. In the evenings we'd climb to the sunset side of the harbour and watch the sky soften into pinks and pale blues: then walk through the darkling village in quest of fish and chips and cider.

54

Possible to stay with Mrs Dorf only for a few days: then she had more guests booked. As the state of total sunshine became more certain, the sky blue as if it would never change, we decided we must stay a day or so more, somewhere. A council house in the village promised to take us in: and Mrs Dorf lent us, to take our bags down there, the rickety soap box on wheels she used for shopping.

'Do come again next year, ducks,' Mrs Dorf insisted, plainly much taken with Kate. I reflected on the fact that my liking for Kate increased every time it became clear that she was liked by someone else. It seemed wrong. It was rather as if I had a greater appreciation of her on finding that she cost three shillings than when I believed she cost, say, two shillings and ninepence. Mrs Dorf's perpetual cigarette puffed farewell at us from the shining porch, and we ran downhill into the village laughing like schoolchildren, Kate lending her bottom, and the weight of our invisible child, as a brake when the slope was sharpest.

I turned from Neill to Donne. 'Enjoy your summer, all,' he cried, across nearly four centuries of weather. We went on the sea, at last—the desire to be on it and part of it had been scarcely bearable: and a storm gathered, with no apparent connection with what came before and after, and we had a wild rocking cold journey across St Austell Bay, in light so leaden that it gleamed like the reverse of sunshine: the white cones of the spoil from the china clay mines becoming the scenery of a nightmare. Out of the sullen cloud came gannets, hurling themselves straight at the sea. 'They have terrible eyes,' said the boatman.

The sun came back at once, as full as before. On our last evening we sat on the cliff, eating fish and chips, and watched, with the concentration of spies, the changes in the sea. Within the one sea, we noted, there were scores of different kinds of sea. It was so still that the white patches marking the currents looked like drying areas on a wet pavement. In one quarter, the outgoing tide produced the effect of insects scurrying across the surface. A dozen small boats seemed embedded in the sea, rather than riding upon it. Then, towards the horizon, a central sea formed, lime and saffron in colour, and smooth as milk. This milky saffron sea spread until it covered the whole of the horizon: then it turned gold. Now the middle stretch turned green, and a thickening purple mist formed along the sky's edge.

55

The headland towards the falling sun was already violet. The golden further sea turned an autumnal brown. A little fishing boat far out upon it looked like a red pyramid in a desert.

Still. So still that when a motor boat came racing towards the harbour, the ripples of its wake filled square miles. They would never be smoothed out. There wasn't the movement of air or water ever to remove those fanning flaws from the sea . . .

We made love laughing and sighing, it must be the last time almost because Kate's belly was itself Cornish, a cone of china clay. We smelt of sunshine and seaweed. It should, I said, be part of the holiday brochure: the promise of love-making so summer-smelling. A seagull guffawed as I spoke—that humourless cackle. 'This is no place to make jokes,' said the melted remains of this girl, Kate, who so strangely was my wife.

The weather changed as we returned to London. Dawlish looked a grey hell inhabited by fierce tall creatures of red rock. London itself was flat . . . and very pale.

12

Eastbourne Road School was as fearsomely solid as when I'd first seen it, a foursquare trap for echoes as I trudged up the stairs. From above came squeaks and squeals and rumbles, and sudden shouts. The juniors were on the first floor, above the faintly tittering level of the infants. But this morning the autumn sun was shining through the wire mesh on the windows. Nets of shadow writhed on the sour walls. There was dust dancing around me, and a child rushing across the hall had a head that flamed.

I was confided to Mr Barlow.

Curious, where everything was desperate, to be taken to a classroom that was orderly and serene, and to meet a teacher who was not even faintly crazed. But Mr Barlow's was the top class. All those in it had hopes of the grammar school. They went about their academic business, I was to find, like a roomful of clerks. Just going in there, for the first time, one thought: How very like a well-run office! Mr Barlow was totally efficient—goodhumoured but watchfully so: his jokes, one felt, always had some instructive charge in them. A pleasant man. Pleasant and bright faces . . .

Then his class walked out quietly for assembly, and other classes tumbled out. There were collisions, and snarling rebukes. There was the rough taking of places, and rough responses to cries of 'Sit!': and the discovery of errors in spacing, and a guffawing shuffle of bottoms, leading to greater errors yet: and bitter outbursts from an elderly teacher on the platform: and an exhausted pause: and then the appearance of two late classes. One, led by a youngish man who was shouting, 'Oh, belt up, you *curs*!', made its way to a part of the floor that all the shuffling and spreading and squeezing up had left occupied. It came slowly, blindly, hands in pockets, talking loudly, not at school at all: if anywhere, on the broad pavements of the local High Street on a Saturday afternoon. Finding that the space it had chosen was occupied, it came to a baffled, chattering halt. 'Up here! up here!' howled the teacher, dancing up and down on an empty patch of floor to the rear of the now re-excited assembly. The successfully squeezed up began to spread, the spread to squeeze up. The tardy class gave what was almost a single start, and frowned almost a single frown: dug its hands deeper into its pockets, and began to make its way towards the empty space, but across and tramplingly over rows of boys already seated. There was a terrible impression of bones snapping. It was the cue for the last class of all to appear. It belonged to the man I'd met on my first visit, the apoplectic teacher with strained eyes. His class came, hopping and shrieking, as he dived for its legs with a ruler. 'Get on . . . we're late,' he shouted. 'You're late, Mr Flynn!' cried the elderly teacher on the platform. This last class rushed unsteadily, leaping and squealing, towards the most thickly populated area of the angry floor; while I wondered if there were any primary school equivalent of martial law.

And then, when the headmaster was in place, the oddest thing happened. The old teacher on the platform produced a violin-case. The school was to be led in its singing with a violin, not with a piano. It seemed strange, in this furious scene—even, in some grotesque fashion, moving. He opened the case; and I saw that in the lid, alongside the bow, held by its loops of leather, other loops had been added, and that these held a cane . . .

It was, somehow, the mark of Eastbourne Road: violin bow and cane, side by side. My unrepresentative home in the building was with Mr Barlow—who, with his bright boys, didn't really belong. But I spent much time, in the first day or so, with Mr Small, the violinist.

He was on the point of retiring: a man who'd become simply a bundle of queer tired habits. His teaching was one long plaint, in growling Cockney. Though he wore spectacles, these seemed barely to help him to see. He peered through them blindly, as if they'd been obstacles rather than aids. At times he would pause, mouth open, and remain so for moments on end, while the class rustled around him. He seemed to be attempting to understand where he was, and why. Then he would be with us again: would shake his head and utter, in the direction of the whispering boys, a long, loud 'Aaarghhh!' 'Aaarghhh! What's that, then? Who's that, then? Who's at it, eh? Who's trying it on, eh?' He might, at this point, address himself. 'You've never known anything like it, 'ave you? Not in all your years of teaching.'

The first lesson was Scripture. Having announced that this was so, Mr Small opened a cupboard and rummaged among the books it contained. He found a Bible and turned the pages, groaning to himself. 'We've 'ad *that* . . . We won't 'ave *that* . . . You'll 'ave *that* in the top class . . . Well, *this'll* do. Now, shut up, sit up and listen. Keep your arms on the desk where I can see them. Straight, straight, *straight*! If I catch anyone leaning on the next boy I'll come and lean on *'im*!' He fell into one of his blind pauses. Then: 'All right. This is about Jacob. 'Oo was Jacob? No, don't try to tell me. None of you know. You're ignorant, the lot of you. None of you know 'oo Jacob was.' He glared at them over his glasses, as though to make this statement was the point of his lesson. 'Just get that into your thick 'eads— none of you know 'oo Jacob was. You're ignorant. Got it?'

The class rustled absent-mindedly. Most boys seemed to have adjusted to Mr Small. They were quiet enough—for if they

58

weren't, he'd pounce with a ruler, rushing here and there and banging at legs, knuckles and heads. Then the class would become hedgehogs, rolling themselves up against that angry length of wood. But they weren't there, very much. They laughed weakly, if laughter seemed to be called for : or put doubtful hands in the air, if there seemed to be a question. On the whole, though, they attended to their own inner affairs.

Mr Small read the story of Jacob's dream, with lapses into paraphrase. He was not an expressive reader : there was a curious resemblance to someone quoting from a railway timetable. He made comments as he went along—largely, astonished comments of a non-theological nature. "'E laid 'is 'ead on some stones—that must 'ave been pretty 'ard.' The remark wasn't addressed to the boys : their absent-mindedness was unaffected. With surprise, I saw that he was talking to me where I sat, hoping I was inconspicuous, in a corner of the room. 'Pretty 'ard,' he insisted. 'My goodness, yes,' I called. 'Well, it says so 'ere, so I suppose we 'ave to believe it,' said Mr Small. An expression of reluctant surrender that seemed hardly to be in the spirit of the Agreed Syllabus for Religious Education . . .

Sad old man ! I lost touch with him very quickly as the morning wore on : in this respect being, evidently, a typical member of the class. From Scripture, somehow, he got to the Gunpowder Plot. It was ten minutes of History, in which, as with the story of Jacob, he seemed to be talking to himself. I gathered that he had doubts, which no historical testimony could allay, as to the course of events in that old drama. 'Well, they say someone told on him. I suppose they're right. I suppose that's what 'appened . . .' He brought his brooding to an end with a cry of : 'Well, that's that !—get your sum books out and 'ave a go at that lot'—reversing the blackboard like a tired magician to reveal half a dozen sums.

Some of these habits of his, into which his teaching had plainly declined, seemed to refer to old teaching situations that no longer existed. It didn't seem strictly necessary, for example, that there should be only one piece of blotting paper in the room, which he himself took from boy to boy. Separated from it at one point, he cried : 'Who's the silly squirt who's got that blotting paper?' He obeyed some inner timetable, nothing to do with the formal one pinned to a cupboard door : 'Time I taught you on the

c 59

blackboard.' He used threatening phrases too worn to have any menace left in them—yet their frequency gave to the room, to his weary pacing of it, a lowering air. It was the air of . . . a nagging headache. When he set them to work on some wretched piece of dictation : 'If you've begun with a small "t", don't be surprised if I rear up and whack you one !'

But I saw Mr Small out in the hall, the first morning, conducting a singing lesson. It was a poor sort of yelling, really. Queer scene : four ragged classes of imps and gnomes, ready at any moment to screech an approximate version of a folk song. And Mr Small, scraping at his violin, and listening to the music, or perhaps to the music behind the unhappy sounds he made, with the most strange, *affectionate* expression on his face.

13

I had this odd feeling about all my three school practices . . . that they were versions of execution. You stood against the school wall and, in a long-drawn out fashion—it took a month each time—you were shot. With the firing squad becoming increasingly impatient, there was the incessant possibility of appeals, in the execution yard itself. These were lessons when you were observed by your visiting tutor.

At Eastbourne Road, he was Green : who took us, back at Isleden, for P.E. I knew him only as a kind of human dart of a fellow, constantly projecting himself across the gym : usually leading with some sharp end, hands or legs beautifully but unnaturally glued together. I thought of the gym at Isleden simply as the place where all the college dust collected, to be mopped up by, quite largely, me. P.E. I regarded as a process of becoming horrifically dirty. Green clearly had a quite different view of it. Now he appeared, with a sort of hasty elegance, in the equally dusty world of Eastbourne Road, and adjudicated on my appeal against being professionally shot.

I didn't know what to make of the experience, at all. I mean, the general experience of being at the school, in this singular role of student teacher. I found the district so dismaying, to begin with. 'An insult to man,' said my diary of this ancient suburb. 'Full of stinks and filth. Nothing in it but is ugly and degraded . . . the dereliction and greasiness of its long rows of blackened houses, and the school rising in its midst, visible a long way off, and as discouraging as a prison.

'And the heartbreakingly neglected little children, in their grime and tatters and with their squints or pasty faces. Some of them are irresistible little imps; and it's queer that many of the faces are merging into boys' faces I knew at—'

At the prep school five miles away where I'd taught before going to Isleden. It was odd, this facial confusion. More than that—it was a confusion as to actual temperaments, natures, physical habits. A boy wearing some intricately holed jumper—it looked as though he'd been faced with an execution squad, too —ducked his head when he smiled, exactly like young Turnbull at The Vale, dapper and expensive little Turnbull, perfectly hole- less of jumper. The affection I'd felt for boys *up there* (the up- ness was geographical, but didn't now seem to be entirely that) was switched to their doubles *down here*. I'd delivered a lesson on Hengist and Horsa to a class at Eastbourne Road that received the information about those remote characters as if it had been the latest news. They sighed and groaned and smiled at suitable moments in my exposition : one might have thought the threat from Jutland was still alive. A boy had come up to me after the—couldn't call it a lesson ! unprofessional outburst of personal amazement at the idea of Hengist and Horsa ever existing—and said : 'Thanks for the story, sir.' And that was *very* much like The Vale.

I was dismayed by much that was said in the staffroom. Well, *staffroom* ! It was a cupboard in which, if we were all gathered together, we stood sideways, and generated an anger or excitable foolishness that I now recognise to be a consequence of over- crowding. We were shrill-nerved sardines. Much that was said about teaching while I was at Eastbourne Road was obviously inspired, or provoked, by my presence. I was harmless, confused,

61

conventional enough. But a student was capable of being a standard-bearer for new ideas, new methods; and I was astonished to observe that such things were held to be the cunning property of training college lecturers and inspectors. Having such ideas was the essential condition of their *being* lecturers and inspectors. It seemed to occur to no one how disheartening it might have been for a teacher in training, to be present at such attacks on the whole notion of novelty and freshness in teaching.

The dreary roots of this staffroom objection to any idea of professional renewal were exposed by the conduct of the laziest man on the staff: who, on the very first day of my visit, made a vague gesture in the direction of his pupils and colleagues and said: 'Imagine forty years of that!' Difficult to exceed the dreariness of dismissing a whole professional lifetime as a misery!— a misery, moreover, for us both (for he too was under thirty), that was yet to be experienced! If at times I thought in terms of execution yards, it was partly because I had this picture of teachers who'd lashed themselves to their stakes, and made their last, extremely drab wishes known, in their late twenties or early thirties.

Well, as to him, this dreariest and laziest of men! Early in my stay at Eastbourne Road, I'd found myself in his classroom —'a film-strip lesson,' he told me. 'I've got this film-strip. Nineteenth century, we're doing.' He hadn't bothered to look at it before the lesson began, and so we sat, in the darkened room, and he peered at the explanatory booklet, trying to give himself something like a fifteen second warning of the picture that was to come. His favourite cry was: 'Put up your hands anyone who . . .' The class rioted. But, being nine years old, most of them, they didn't so much riot as express their natural boredom. He was not with them, and they were not remotely with him. They withdrew into their own chattering, chuckling world, and I felt disgraced, seeming to be attached to him but longing to express my real allegiance: which, in that situation, was most certainly to them, by simple attraction to the ill-done-by.

It was indeed nineteenth century history that, without their participation, he was covering. There was a picture, among them all, of a slum street. It came up on the screen before he was ready, but he caught up with it, saying: 'This is a typical slum street of the nineteenth century. Look at it, now. Put up your hands anyone who . . .' And it did not occur to him that, if he had lifted the blinds and directed the children to look out at Eastbourne Road, the surrounding scene would have fairly matched the one on the strip of film that had taken him by surprise.

Green came and saw me conducting a lesson on areas. It was with Barlow's class, and their habitual, eleven-plus-expecting good manners had been reinforced by a speech about the consequences they could expect from behaving badly. Anyone who behaved badly would . . . but it wasn't imaginable. Mr Barlow and his class acknowledged the unimaginability of it, given his directive. My lesson seemed to me horribly woolly : I felt that, if I'd been a member of the class, I'd have been bored and puzzled. But as I bared my chest to Green's bullet, I was astonished to hear him say, absolutely refusing to press the trigger : 'With a little hard work, there's no reason why you shouldn't pass out of Isleden an A teacher.' It was the first time I'd understood you could do this. I hadn't gathered that your teacherliness might be defined as A, B, C and so forth.

I was awfully happy. Well, I was still alive. But I was awfully unhappy, too. Because Green was quite obviously, quite amazingly wrong.

The lino on the staffroom floor was pitted as though, when it was still in a molten state, cast-iron ping-pong balls had been dropped all over it. I worried about this over many dull exhausted breaks until I concluded that through the years the furniture must have been ceaselessly on the move. How many table legs, how many chair legs, would be needed to make all those little pits ! The general colouring was a choking brown, as elsewhere in the school—though round the dead grate there'd been a sudden betrayal of this colour, in the form of tiles, viciously blue. Long ago there'd actually been wallpapering, plain material of a brown particularly morose : divided into panels by a sort of frieze featuring what appeared to be several thousand chocolate-brown navels.

I tried often to imagine the orders that went out to secure this profoundly miserable result. I bothered similarly over a picture in one of the classrooms.

The walls in this room were bare of almost everything but

63

drawing pins, but at the back was this picture, which I at once recognised. Years before it had hung somewhere in one of my own earliest classrooms. A fort was being attacked; the defenders, in large peaked caps, were thrusting down at the attackers, robed and burnoused. The central character was one of the defenders, a man with an elaborate moustache, under whose chin a shell had exploded. At the heart of a cloud of smoke his head was flung back. I remembered staring at this picture as a child, vaguely disturbed because the action was never completed. The soldier with the moustache never blew apart, none of the bayonets ever found its mark.

What struck me now was that it must once have been a favourite among educationists—and how odd that was. I tried to imagine them requisitioning it in quantities: '100 copies of the vicious and disturbing picture of the man with his head being blown off. For distribution among primary school class-rooms.'

They must, though, have looked at it differently? They must have seen in it something to which they wished to direct the attention of very small children?

That was Flynn's classroom. He was in his early forties—an emergency trainee in his first working year—and perhaps the saddest man I met during these thirteen months. He was the emergency trainee exemplified: the man who'd seized the apparent opportunity with the most passionate hopefulness. What seemed to be offered was the chance of escaping from the world of commerce, which he'd found cold and self-concerned, into the world of some sort of direct service to minds and spirits. He would shape human beings! But it didn't happen: because his general vision of the educational world, and himself in it, included no notion of the actual complex intractability of human beings, when it came to being shaped. So Flynn was reduced to the misery (it's too mild a word) of beating children on the legs with his every-morning ruler.

But my admiration for him was great. At the end of one of those lessons of his that became, whatever he tried to do, noisy tangles of rage on his part and mischief on theirs, he ordered them to line up at the door—'like mice,' he groaned, 'not elephants.' And they elected to go to the door exactly like mice

—on tiptoe, faintly squeaking. And Flynn smiled—a tired sweet smile that I've never forgotten.

I admired him for that wry understanding of the irony of things that made him smile, painfully, in the face of farcical failure. And the failure *was* farcical, as is that of all teachers in his condition : consisting as it did (and does) in the earnest adult being reduced to a ludicrous, howling idiot by, at most, forty tiny creatures.

14

There were, that autumn, days as great as the summer's : the sun everywhere, thick as honey. Sometimes, in the morning, there was a little breeze, and when I left home there'd be the shadows of the last leaves leaping on the ground. Half an hour, and leaves would be far behind. Instead, the quick crazy sound of children's voices, like a sharp incoming sea. The school was a rock in that sea, a solid thing washed and worn by generations of children.

'I can still cut a boy's arse off,' said a voice in the staffroom. 'You don't cut an arse off,' said another. 'You cut it *through*.' It was an odd, horrid pedantry to begin the day with.

There was a supply teacher. He was reading *Treasure Island*. I noticed how dull his reading was, how much too fast, how incapable he seemed to be of raising his eye from the page : how dreadfully he interrupted the story with questions. Another sort of horrid pedantry. He left the room and I took over, confidently. I found at once that my voice was too soft, that I was reading too fast. The class had dodged away from me at the moment of handover, and I passed instantly from confidence to unease. I interrupted the story with banal teacherly outcries. Jim Hawkins was in the apple barrel and I was asking : 'Who's talking?' '*You* are, sir.'

Yes, I had this voice without an edge, it was the wrong sort of voice for that part of the world—I'd not realised what blurred gentility there was in it. And I was so roundabout and grand. Ben had made a joke about this, a couple of years before, when we were walking towards Wales. 'I talk like a book? Show me what you mean,' I'd demanded, as we shuffled down the back-side of the Long Mynd into Shropshire. 'The increasing architec-tural density,' Ben volunteered, 'implies urban proximity . . .' Well, yes, I had to agree—that was the spirit of much that I said, and it was quite wrong for Eastbourne Road.

I laboured every evening on my lesson notes. Only Kate's cheerfulness lightened my gloom. She was cheerful partly because she wasn't going to Eastbourne Road next day: but she was cheerful also as a matter of comradely principle, and I was deeply grateful for that. I'd feel, after scratching together my notes on some lesson on the importance of light to health: or the conversion of sq. ins. into sq. ft. and sq. ins.: or the value of meat to Argentina . . . I'd feel as tired and grey of mind as if I'd spent an evening in prison.

'I must,' lamented my diary, 'be a halfwit.' Surely it was half-witted to take so long to do something so simple! Well . . . I see now that, an improvisor by nature, I'd never have been able to teach well on the basis of any evening's anxious planning. I wasn't in fact going to teach with any sensation of success at all until I'd been around in schools long enough to be able to teach on impulse, and had worn through all sorts of baffled formal notions of what a teacher was.

But there had to be a wearing through, I guess, a slow painful being wrong in order to have some chance later of being less wrong. Part of the useless preparation might, with the passing of time, turn out to have been useful preparation?

A curious nightmare, a first teaching practice . . . moving, as a student must, within the narrow scope of single lessons and other people's routines. Like painting somebody else's picture with somebody else's brush, on a third person's canvas, and having it all taken away after thirty-five minutes, at most.

Or you worked with somebody else's triumphant idea, and it fell flat. That happened when I had Kunz's class for a whole morning. He was the teacher I'd met on my first visit, who'd proposed that I take a lesson on the Argentine. He had a huge face that life seemed to have battered at quite brutally, redden-

66

ing his large nose, breaking his teeth, tearing his hair out in a haphazard fashion. He was a man given to a sort of peremptory, weary kindness. Being nice to you, offering staccato advice, he frowned forbiddingly.

Having his class that morning, I'd intended that, like classes all over London being conducted by Isleden students, they should be introduced to the amazing pleasures of choral verse speaking by way of two poems that had been enormously successful . . . at Isleden. It turned out to be like taking a pair of beautiful women to a party and finding that no one wanted to look at them once, let alone twice. I dragged the class, indeed, very little distance beyond the title of the first poem : *Bad Sir Brian Botany* —which made them fall about, with an effect of their discerning in it inscrutable shades of indecent meaning. For a wild moment I wondered if there might be in the class some ragged and impertinent little baronet of that name . . . I tried to read the poem to them and they wept with an amusement that had nothing to do with its content. Behind my shouts lay the helplessness of being unable to spot any precise cause of their appalling pleasure. I announced that they had only themselves to blame if I switched to arithmetic—realising as I did so that it was I who'd be punished if the switch was made. My bluff was drawn; but arithmetic only changed their noisy delight into noisy dismay.

The awfulness of the morning deepened as it went on. It had not been so bad at the very beginning, when I'd decided to discuss with them the parable of the house built on sand. On this I'd embarked fairly eagerly, confident that I understood the architectural basis of the parable. Well—build a house on sand, and obviously it wouldn't stand up long. As I drew this foolish edifice on the board, I felt suddenly uneasy. In terms of my own understanding of what was involved, wouldn't the house make its builders aware of the folly of their efforts long before it was completed? But I thrust the doubt away and showed, in a series of sketches, how the sand slid away from under the house, and how it sank.

In the afternoon, I had the relief of handing over to Kunz and, bruised with misery, listening to him from the back of the room. What a long way I was from being a teacher ! I even found that I was learning from Kunz's lesson almost as much as

67

the class did. It struck me that I'd find it much easier to qualify as a primary school pupil than as a secondary school teacher.

Some time during the afternoon, ill chance brought up the question of desert housing. A matter of tents, said Kunz. A boy chose to show off recent learning. 'Not houses,' he cried. 'They'd sink.' There was a murmur of general assent. '*Sink*? What d'yer mean, *sink*? They wouldn't! What do you know about it?' Kunz demanded, with his habitual tired irony.

All eyes turned to me. 'This teacher said so,' the boy cried, adding accusing finger to accusing eyes.

Kunz politely hurried on, while at the back of the room I quietly slipped my neck into this noose and jumped off this imaginary chair . . .

On Friday afternoons I went back to Isleden, for rehearsals of *Macbeth*. Arnold was having trouble with Rumble, who was playing Young Siward. To Rumble, the play was *The Tragedy of Young Siward*. He pestered Arnold endlessly for advice on how to make himself perfectly different from Old Siward.

Bing was gloomy. Mr Trellis had been present at a lesson in which Bing was concerned with the adjective. 'I never thought I should find myself hating a part of speech so thoroughly.' His hatred had communicated itself to the class. Then Mr Trellis had leapt up and read them a poem—it sounded like Browning, said Bing—and the function of the adjective became triumphantly clear. Mr Trellis had made the adjectives sound like bells and the class had sat there, beaming. 'I never thought I should find myself hating children so much.'

Broom was gloomier. He'd been visited by Mr Jepp, who'd subjected his lesson to a withering analysis. 'I'd much rather he'd got the kids to hold me down and then hit me with a sledgehammer,' said Broom. 'I told him I'd never stood up and talked in a classroom until two days before—and that I didn't mind criticism, but this was murder.' It had seemed to him that Mr Jepp's famous eyes had come very close to being unseated, after that.

Capper showed us his lesson notes. At the foot of each lesson we were required to describe, frankly, how it had gone. The usual tone of these comments was one of restrained chagrin, or very careful satisfaction. In this field, as in others, Capper was

68

different. He was bold beyond belief. Of one of his lessons he'd written :

'You could have heard a pin drop.'

It was Bing's suggestion that the image might have been drawn from logging. For 'pin', given Capper's lack of ease in spelling, one should perhaps read 'pine'.

15

There was the problem, for which I wasn't at all prepared, of having total, non-teaching strangers in the classroom.

The first was a glazier. He was at work on cracked window panes. It was as if, conducting an orchestra, I'd discovered that there was a riveter going round among the music stands, carrying out repairs. The glazier was a severe-looking man, who didn't seem much to like the boys. He glanced at them bleakly, from time to time. He didn't seem to care enormously for me. On my entrance, after what must have been an incredulous scowl, I smiled nervously at him. But he stared blankly back. There was obviously to be no acknowledgement even of the fact that he was in the room.

Damn it, I thought, as all eyes wandered to his hands, cleverly busy with putty. How could I compete with a glazier? How could I compete with any man engaged in practical work? I very much wanted to watch him myself. He could remove a cracked window pane from its frame with a few taps with the tip of a trowel. Amazing . . .

But it was I who was in the room to be amazing, with the story of Alfred the Great. *Subject: History*, said my lesson notes. Class 6 ('B') Boys. *No. in class:* 34. *Average Age:* $7\frac{1}{2}$–$8\frac{1}{2}$. *Duration of lesson:* 35 mins. *Relevant knowledge:* Nil. There should have been a further heading: *Fly in the Ointment:* Presence of a gifted, glum glazier.

The right-hand page of my notes was divided down the middle, and one of the resulting columns was headed *Teaching Board:* the other, *Semi-Permanent Record.* I'd often thought how odd that use of the term 'semi-permanent' was, since it described, in many cases, deathless monuments of model-making . . . dodeca-hedrons of such construction that they'd have outlived, clearly, any mere blackboard. I had, for this lesson, several items of Semi-Permanent Record.

'Pin up S.P.R. picture of Viking ship,' my notes began. 'Explain that over 1,000 years ago, had they been little English boys, they would have been terrified at the sight of one of these. But a king rose in England who fought the Danes : and it is his story they are going to hear.

'*Stress* that in those days few people could read because there were no schools. . . .'

I pinned up the picture of the Viking ship. It had been coloured by Kate, in hues that now struck me as—chintzy. It was, somehow, a Viking ship straight out of my lady's boudoir. The glazier gave it a severe glance in the middle of a rapid routine of puttying. I read his expression dismally. 'So this is what History had degenerated to in our schools. The Vikings as decorations on . . . sofa cushions. That ship would sink at once under the weight of uncut moquette.'

When I mentioned the illiteracy of Alfred's day, and ascribed this to the absence of schools, I read satire into the way the glazier ran his trowel, little cynical bangings, round the edge of a newly-inserted pane. 'Damned lucky if you ask me, *not* to have schools, I can't wait to get out and ring the papers about this . . .'

Long before the lesson was over I was talking, more or less, out of the corner of my mouth—trying to exclude my critic on his ladder. He remained grim to the end—even, as I tried to get them to leave the room in an orderly fashion, staring at me for a long moment, as if memorising my face for reasons connected with the possibility of some later hue and cry.

During the whole of my second week at Eastbourne Road, a sanding machine was at work in the hall and then in classroom after classroom, taking off the top of floors. It was an immense rasping and snarling. But these were only the more dramatic interruptions. There was an endless succession of smaller ones :

boys bearing messages, regiments of district nurses wishing to examine hair, incoherent mothers offering excuses for their absent sons, mothers very coherent indeed checking on probable truants, the headmaster in vagrant mood . . .

I was suddenly certain that I would not be passed out as a teacher. This activity was so very odd, and nothing like teaching as I'd imagined it—or, at the prep school, known it. Barlow had the gift for it—that good, neat man, with his black hair oiled into place, and the brisk orderliness of his classroom, and his mastery of decimals, long division and the identification of parts of speech. My admiration for Barlow was real, but I'd never be good at what he was good at. Green had seen me again, and I read a sinister meaning into his statement: 'I'm not worrying about you'. No point in worrying about what was so far beyond repair? But, he said, I ought to tighten up on my discipline. I really was rather too kindly. 'You seem to have taken a stand against bullying them. Well, a bit of the right kind of bullying is necessary, I think you'll find. You must have silence, you see, when you want it. Nothing to worry about. But think about it.'

Silence! I had, hadn't I, this curious nervous dread of causing my classes to be silent! Partly it was because, once having brought about that condition, I couldn't believe it could be sustained. Better to bring it to an end myself than wait, nerve-racked, for its natural collapse. Partly my dread was based, I thought, on my feeling for the boys. I liked the mischief and the life in them. Making them silent filled me with absurd guilt. I was afraid of putting an end to the entire human capacity for joy. I dreaded the idea of becoming qualified for thirty years' employment as a spoilsport.

Anyway, whenever the Head wandered in, among all those other forms of interruption, it was always when there quite definitely wasn't silence in the room. Except, ridiculously, once when I'd been taking a lesson on the geography of Wales, with Flynn's class, and had drifted from the mention of mountains in my lesson notes to a mention, not sanctioned by that document, of mountaineering, and men falling to their death and being preserved in the ice, and slowly, for years and years, being carried by glaciers down to the sea. I was ashamed of the ease with which I abandoned the strict matter of my lesson, and dwelt on the ghoulish details of frozen death, drawn to do so by the sudden transformation of a fidgeting class, not impressed by Welsh geography, into a class totally attentive, very much impressed indeed by the idea of a refrigerated mountaineer. The headmaster came in and cried: 'Class 3 is very attentive! Class 3 is being a very good class this afternoon! Carry on like this, Class 3!' Then to me, after glancing at the map of Wales on the board: 'Fascinating! Fascinating! "Dear mother of minstrels!"' I confused the quotation with a cry of pain on his part, and was moving towards him solicitously when I saw what he meant, and covered my embarrassment with a hideous grin.

Mr Trellis was to come with Green to observe my last concert performance at Eastbourne Road: yet another lesson on decimals with Class 5.

It was strange having him at the back of the class: like being visited by some famous statue. The lesson went with dull decency until I set the class what was to be the first of a series of little outbursts of work. To my surprise, Mr Trellis instantly leapt to his feet and began to dash round the room, peering over boys' shoulders. He uttered cries of encouragement and correction: paused to make sallies with a blue pencil, to pat heads, chaff some and subject others to long, sorrowful stares. Everywhere he seemed to be proposing extra examples for them to work on. I found myself moving round the class at his heels, at the same tempo. It was as if we were obeying the measure of some subliminal tarantella. I uttered cries, too, patted heads . . . This episode in the lesson was going on far longer than was laid down in my notes. After five minutes, I was to have commanded pens to be put down, eyes to be fixed on me. But at that point Mr Trellis was hardly through the first figure of this educational *pas de deux* into which he had converted the lesson. He kept it up, with an increasingly manic excitement—which I reflected precisely—until a moment before the bell. Then *he* told them to put their pens down, and to fix their eyes on *him*, and gave them a quick, amused, strict lecture, perfectly in his style, absolute Trellis: the voice gentle and warm with that undertone of severity that was so oddly attractive. He darted up to me, when it was all over and they'd gone, made a shy windmill of his arms —said 'You've nothing to worry about'—and danced away.

Bing and Broom and I compared notes on that first school practice. Deeply uneasy, we discovered that we'd all been given the same reassurance, in the same words.

We had nothing to worry about.

PART TWO

1

Mr Trellis launched the second part of the course with an ambiguously gentle, rather long speech that ignored teaching practice and reached back to the holiday that had preceded it. He seemed to be at once in favour of holidays and immensely opposed to them. He hoped that, as to the studies we'd been busy with, we'd returned with our minds refreshed : but he seemed to fear that they might also be minds emptied. He thrashed us with kindly smiles, while at his side Mr Jepp's explosive eyes issued their own frightful welcome.

Broom pointed out that Mr Trellis seemed more than ever to be all wrists and hands. Those hands now provided an incessant visual aid to the punctuation of his utterances. Broom said we might have noticed he didn't ever go very close to the principal nowadays, for fear of injury. 'It would be absurd to be given a black eye or a bloody nose by a comma.'

'But,' said Bing, 'such a courteous comma.'

And indeed, Mr Trellis was courtesy itself. Many were made guilty, even restive, by the purity of his good manners. He'd arrive among us, say at a serving hatch at a morning break, and smile with such strict sweetness—among those shoving elbows, be so plainly a non-shover—address men with such accuracy as to their names—that a sort of irritability underlay the admiration he caused . . .

Now he rounded off his speech with sadly smiling remarks on shoving at serving hatches, and so forth.

Jack Hagger told us about his visit to Hungary. He talked of it as if it had been fairyland. It was difficult, without being churlish, to demur at the enthusiastic images he offered, of people whose spirits shone with total ideological happiness. He did not speak like a man making arguable propositions. His own

77

face glowed. Describing the streets of Budapest, he talked of 'solidarity' and 'brotherhood' as if they had been festive masks the people were wearing. I've never known another man who could use abstract words with such an effect of describing things that were plainly visible and tangible and carnival-coloured.

'The *determination* . . . and the *unity*—you should really go and see for yourself. The sense of *achievement*! The *socialist pride*!'

'But Jack—'

One didn't want to tie one's doubt to the people of Budapest. In relation to any place whatever, such assertions of complete political euphoria would surely qualify for a little sceptical scrutiny?

Capper claimed to have stayed at home during the holiday weeks, working on his thesis on James Joyce. This had already become a legend in the college. As far as could be made out, he'd read practically nothing of Joyce. Just before the holiday, astonished by the news that the first instalment of his study ought to be delivered by the end of the week ('Jesus wept!'), he had consulted a biographical dictionary and begun copying from it. After two or three sentences he grew clamorously weary, and turned to kicking the furniture. One more sentence, and his capacity for close study was exhausted. He stormed off to throw a ball about somewhere.

Arnold insisted that we be shown the product of Capper's holiday labours. Take away the handmade and quite beautifully decorated folder (the work of Mrs Capper), a frontispiece typed by Capper himself in a style that might economically be called Misprint, and a collection of photos of Joyce and his friends that looked suspiciously as though they'd been ripped from a library book, and you were left with three quarters of a page of thesis. In these few sentences, we found, Capper's hero was born and buried. Arnold said: 'Really, you needn't do any more. It's all there. One of the most charming *small* critical studies ever written—and if I may say so, most refreshingly free both of criticism and of study.' Capper stared at him, smiled, and struck him a friendly blow that, had it landed an inch to left or right, might well have been fatal.

Knowing Capper was one of the more dangerous aspects of the course.

Rumble had only been to Ramsgate (the 'only' was his), but had derived from this humble holiday greater advantages than could be offered by Hungary or, Rumble seemed to suggest, by Heaven itself.

But in fact, I thought—suddenly understanding, a little, what it was to be Mr Trellis, often to be seen collecting abandoned teacups—the college *was* exceedingly bad-mannered, on the whole. It was perhaps the wartime experience that made it so. You jostled because for years you'd known that if you didn't, you'd be the loser. Using your elbows had become a way of life.

And it wasn't a physical thing, only. Lots of inner elbows, as it were, of personality and character, were busily at work, seeking to drive their owners to the front in the struggle for approval, success, importance. It was the other side of the truth that many emergency trainees brought with them a special determination, an unusual sincerity in their wish to be teachers. They were also driven by largely unspoken anxieties. Normal development had been so long delayed. The war was an endless queue and we'd all been held up in it, an experience that left the soul stiff, cramped, afflicted with angry pins and needles. Emergency trainees were being apprentices at an age when many of their old serving friends had dropped out of the queue and back into established positions in offices, banks, shops, the professions. They were exposing themselves to the sometimes humiliating comments of tutors, to tests and inquisitions, and to constant assessment. They longed to be in a state of A-ness, and were in perpetual dread of being found not to have risen above C-ness—even to have sunk to D-ness and E-ness.

At worst, the college made itself felt as a mob of thrustful, irritable egos. The elbowing was wearisome . . .

And when I found myself thinking like this, at the beginning of the second lap, I wondered if I were not myself moved by disgruntled egotism. There'd been, while I was at Eastbourne Road, such a stirring of sulky aspirations. What they brought to the surface was a feeling that working among these ragged children was dreary and ignoble. A desire to be free, to move in colourful and cultivated settings (some such phrases suggested themselves), struggled feebly within me.

Was I taking the course seriously? Did I not fundamentally regard myself as being there by accident? Someone would arrive and say: 'Oh my dear fellow—this is not for you! Come—we've got something rather glorious for you, just round the corner . . .'

Well, I was in a state of C-ness, myself, but worse, as a result of Mr Jepp's assessment of some lesson notes done as a holiday task. The dreadful verdict was, in fact, C *minus*. 'Remote, academic,' he wrote. I observed that he formed his tall letters like stilettoes.

Nothing worse could happen. And it was true—I was far, far from any classroom reality. I could feel my academic character tight about me, a sort of pin-striped skin.

Where was I? I had that bewilderment about myself that I suddenly saw must be experienced by many school children. One teacher thought the world of you: to another you were the most miserable specimen he'd encountered. You lurched from being highly favoured to being hideously frowned upon. It was part of the misery of being young, of being assessed and reported on so constantly and with such baffling inconsistency. Now, at twenty-nine, I was in the thick of it. Mr Salt smiled, and said pleasant things about my essays. But Mr Jepp despised me.

I think he really did, at the time. He had vast scorn for a whole group of us, including Bing and Broom and me. It was all part of what I now see as the paranoia of educational institutions. It was part, also, of what was becoming the stagnant quality of main course lectures in the hall.

What happened is that the most eager students, those concerned at all costs to emerge with unequivocal As, occupied the front rows. It was their rapt faces that any main course lecturer was principally aware of. He looked down and there was this enthusiastic frieze: there were these busy pencils. A fair turn of phrase on his part led at once to notemaking activity on theirs. When he paused they fixed him with hungry eyes. Their names, inevitably, were known to him. He could not but be impressed: or, I think, avoid regarding the rest of his audience as most frightfully inferior.

They must have shaded away, from those attentive front rows, into deeper and deeper indifference. Bing and Broom and I were much towards the back. Broom was usually preoccupied with his

Daily Worker. Bing sometimes set himself mathematical problems of fearsome difficulty, and solved them with modest gasps of self-admiration. I made sketches of my fellow-students. It was the one activity of the kind for which I had a gift, making something of the comedy of faces, and it had become an addiction. I had only to see a face, settled at some fresh angle, to be driven to draw it. It had the tiresome inevitability of any habit, and I wished I could stop. I tried to give up sketching, to become a non-sketcher, but in vain.

At times we would be struck by some phrase of Mr Jepp's and would repeat it admiringly or fool with it satirically. This had nothing to do with any feeling we might have about Mr Jepp and rarely with any opinion of the phrase itself, regarded as a meaningful combination of words. It was, as often as not, the sheer sound that set us off.

Out of Mr Jepp's familiar drone, the educational patter to which we had become essentially deaf, would rise a phrase such as 'the centrality of the curriculum.' 'I knew him once,' Bing might murmur. 'A deeply unhappy man.' 'I was admiring last night,' Broom would sigh, 'the centrality of my friend, Miss Severn.' And once or twice at such a moment, as our faces were seized on by yawning grins, the heads in front of us moved apart and through an accidental rift running the length of the hall Jepp stared straight at us. His stare, on these occasions, grew into a glare. The famous eyes protruded. 'He really is a basilisk,' said Broom once, sharing the idea with us together with a smile : curiously unable to digest the rather simple fact that, at that moment, Jepp's eye was on us. 'We should think,' Jepp had cried, with no change of voice, so that his front-row disciples were startled by what seemed a stormy non-sequitur, 'of these things Plato said . . . whenever we feel inclined to *scoff at things of the mind.*' Broom smiled gently in the afterglow of his own joke, and Jepp's glare became savage.

There it was—we had drifted into seeming, to the powerful Mr Jepp, no better than philistines.

And *that* was some kind of irony, I guess. Because we were alarmed about what we saw as a pervasive philistinism among our fellows.

One of the problems (this is where it seemed to begin) was

81

equating one's sense of humour with other people's. I kept finding myself out of step, in respect of smiles and scowls, when it came to the activities of a jolly band of men who acted, corporately, as the college jester. Their buffoonery was a matter of hard work, always. So they ran a candidate in the sober election for a chairman of the Students' Union; and the election at once ceased to be sober, for posters appeared everywhere, and sandwich boards stalked the corridors, and red noses were distributed widely, the candidate having such a nose : and on the morning of the election, red nose-shaped balloons tumbled into the hall from the gallery. To have their say on some matter or other, the group captured the stage on the brink of a morning assembly, and filled it with a perfectly trained choir which made the group's case in a condensed cantata. Mr Trellis responded to such events with a dangerous sort of indulgence and precarious good humour. You saw his problem. It was high spirits, and to be encouraged. But it had also the powerful and disturbing quality of successful rebellion—the college noticeboards were ruthlessly taken over, the college air ruthlessly filled with balloons or, on another occasion, with hundreds of paper aeroplanes : the college platform was ruthlessly commandeered at the very moment when Mr Trellis was approaching it for religious purposes.

And when it came to their challenge to Hugh Ison, the group made themselves master (having ruthlessly charmed Mr Trellis's secretary) of the college duplicators.

Ison was the college's one indubitable poet. His gift was young, and his work full of echoes, but there was always a freshness even in what was stale in it. He was a modest, good-natured man, and smiled when the group turned him into one of their running jokes. Anyone—it was the implication—could write verse of Ison's kind, simply by making arbitrary raids on the dictionary. I thought the joke a poor one. It could amuse only if you believed Ison really was an impostor—and to think that, you'd have to be blind and deaf and heartless. Beyond this, it could seem funny only if you held that modern verse, of which Ison's was a quietly honest example, was in general the work of pretentious frauds. It was a philistine joke. So I thought.

The challenge to Ison took the form of an offer to publish a poem of his alongside poems they would confect themselves. They would write these, they promised, standing on their heads :

or in their sleep: or by cutting phrases out of magazines and laying them together: or by pricking words at random in a dictionary. The college would then be invited to distinguish the genuine Ison from the forgeries.

Ison agreed: and it was done. Only men with serious brain-damage, I thought, could have failed to make out the wrong 'uns: some of which, it must be said, sorted themselves out at once by being extremely funny, which Hugh Ison never was. Some were simply the silliest pastiche. But the college voted: and overwhelmingly failed to pick the Ison. The group laid on one of its triumphs, like some comic version of a Roman event: in this case literally so, for they constructed a sort of chariot built round a couple of bicycles, and Rumble volunteered to represent Ison, being trotted round the building in chains.

Hugh Ison smiled, a little uncertainly, I thought, and Mr Trellis at the next assembly said, with his mildly disconcerted smile, that literary men like others must learn to adopt a sporting attitude towards challenges to their pretensions.

And I thought it a dreadful joke—coming from teachers, doubly dreadful. What were teachers doing, being philistines? Surely in a classroom philistinism was as much out of place as poison in a kitchen? What were they doing, failing to know—or pretending that they didn't know—honest verse from inexpert parody? What did this imply about the approach to poetry, and literature in general, and important kinds of human seriousness, that they'd take with them into the schools? And wasn't it all, really, a snigger directed against the very idea of poetry, and poets?

There were others who felt the same: Bing and Broom, and Arnold, and the college Marxists, Jack Hagger at their head. But by now I was twitchy about finding myself caught up in certain alliances. There'd been some ugly talking not long before, when George Orwell died. I'd not imagined that the death so early of this gifted man could be regarded as anything but a tragedy. In my naïvety I was astonished when the Stalinists turned out to be positively glad of it. To them, Orwell was simply a renegade. They actually believed that he had sold his gift for money. That was the only reason, Jack said, why *Animal Farm* was written. 'You deny it any virtue?' I cried. 'Mere sneering,' said Jack, in his gentle, kindly voice. 'No literary gift, even?'

This meaningless inquiry made Jack shrug. To Bing he said:
'I can understand you—I think I know why someone like you
becomes a Trotskyist! But Blish! He's full of ideals! I can't
understand *him*!'

2

Ben gazed across the Thames at some ruins on the South Bank.
We were on our way home from the Tate Gallery: where he'd
expressed disappointment in Turner's *Snowstorm at Sea*—he
remembered the real thing, he said, as white of snow against
intense black of sea, not all a whirling white, as here . . . I'd
been talking about Jack Hagger and the Stalinists. Ben was uncertain.

'There's still a lot to be said for the USSR, isn't there?' he
said. 'Surely a workman there is still an important person?'

'But is he? Is he, *really*, any longer?'

'You think he's not?'

'Well, even in this matter of the Russian wives of British serving men not being allowed to join their husbands . . . surely even
in that there's a wealth of ominous meaning?'

'Yes. But I wonder if the women really wanted to come here?
I wonder if they were good marriages. I doubt it. Sexual mirages.
That's what a serving man often suffered from, you know, in
wartime.'

'Oh, but surely we must presume that they were good marriages. Surely that's the essence of'—I floundered for words—
'the liberal attitude?'

'Well,' said Ben. He smiled at the ruins, wryly. 'I suppose there
might have been three or four good marriages among them. But
don't you think that any country might quite fairly regard these
women as more useful to the State than to their wartime
husbands?'

'Oh but . . . Isn't marriage one of those acts in which the law ought to presume that a man has acted wisely? And that he's gained a right by it—the right to live with his wife . . . that's practically inviolable?'

Ben smiled at me, as if I, too, were a ruin of a sort. 'Not everyone,' he said, 'regards marriage as we do.'

But dammit—Ben and I had no shared view of marriage. He, happily committed to it in fact, in theory prowled round it with the utmost suspicion, testing it for flaws. 'I think I have a rival, you know. Marie's always longing for the Loire Inférieure. It's funny to have a whole department of France as the third party. Well, I guess if she went we'd both get over it. People do, don't you think?'

It seemed to me that my own attitude to marriage had been shaped by early reading, and films. Those fairy tales, those romantic stories. I'd always fallen heavily for the idea of marriage. It seemed nice. It made the heart beat faster—in itself a most acceptable sensation—and filled the mind with the idea of shared winter fires, rather specially agreeable companionship in warm settings. And, of course, much more than that. But one of the excellences of it all, as I understood it, was that amazing excitements, and great possibilities of increase in perception and enjoyment of life, were contained in such a delectable envelope. It was the best of all human parcels.

How I'd grieved, and rejoiced, for Dick Dewey in Hardy's *Under the Greenwood Tree*, read in class at school in circumstances that had killed nobler works, *Twelfth Night, As You Like It*, but left this one undefeated. My heart had grown huge, with his, for love of Fancy Day—had shrivelled, like his, at her teasing infidelities. I'd believed in the blinding happiness of their union, at the end. I was obstinately in favour of being happy, in that dazzled fashion.

Perhaps, oh Lord, my view of all that was the emotional equivalent of my newly lost notion of some sort of fixed good?

And what an extraordinary thing it had seemed to be, electing to marry a particular person—and being elected! I remembered an occasion, soon after Kate and I became engaged (a term that Ben worried at, rather), when a sense of the momentousness of these elections rose inside me—literally *rose*, for I could feel it making its way upward through my body like some positive

85

physical column of feeling: an amazement that occupied great, expanding, vertical space inside me. It was too awesome to be borne—this decision to be bound together, to be perpetual companions! What had we done?

It was like blowing up one's whole personal landscape—voluntary self-dynamiting. I was moved beyond coherence—turned to clutch Kate, murmuring words that came from some stunning declaration of awe and . . . dizzy dedication.

The actual event of being married had turned out to be as easy as, when I was a child, Christmas Day had been easy after the nervous eternity of Christmas Eve.

Where weddings were concerned, Kate was a romantic. If it had been possible to imagine Jane Eyre being married in a register office . . . The setting, then, was this charming church, of which I'd made lopsided drawings in childhood: I'd never been able to make it stand quite straight: and it wasn't standing quite straight that morning when, with my atheistical best man, Ben, I wandered—having arrived a little early—among the tombstones. I felt heavily disguised in a sober blue suit, and inclined to clasp my hands behind my back. Ben's neatness was more familiar. Pretending again, I thought, to be a civil servant.

'I've made,' said Ben, 'some purchases, thinking they might be—um—you might be glad of them.'

'Have,' I said, 'some already. Many thanks. Went to . . .'

Had gone, in fact, to Charing Cross Road, which, for the first year of my marriage, I believed to be the only place where contraceptives could be bought. I made, I remember with amazement, the expensive journey from the suburbs in order to visit this quarter: as a home of secondhand books, the Mecca of my youth. There'd been those other establishments tucked in among the bookshops, a kind of glum punctuation for a literary street, trusses displayed, advertisements claiming (with the most unsuitable dreariness) that sparkle and zest could be restored to one's sex life . . . I forgot who, in the end, told me about barber's shops.

Ben said that, in terms of elocution, Kate and I did full credit to the ceremony. 'Your responses were, in fact, quite thrilling,' he said. It seemed absolutely the right thing to say: we felt very much like—well, leading dancers in a ballet: much of the day was spent, so to speak, in front of the Covent Garden curtain : the thud of thrown bouquets became positively monotonous. The problem was that we also felt modest and even a little absurd. We were leading dancers blushing and attempting to shrug off our fame. My blue suit lent itself very readily to notions of unimportance and anonymity. Kate had sat up all night putting finishing touches to a yellow dress of her own design—'I found I was making it up as I went along, and I was so scared,' she said—and on an impulse had sent her father in search of yellow roses, which she wore in her hair. 'I think they were a substitute for straws . . .'

To my father the whole event was not so much a wedding as an act of surrender on my part. It amounted to my philosophical overthrow. At the moment Kate might be smiling on some of my odder ideas : but it was, of course, in the nature of women to be indulgent during courtship and then to clamp down—ah, how eagerly in his head my father must have used that phrase 'clamp down', a favourite of his—once safely wedded. So at the reception he was springy, benign : rather like a prison governor seeing a persistent escaper being brought back loaded with chains.

He made, to my delight, the slyest of speeches. Oddly, he said —as if truly puzzled by this—oddly, a memory had *floated* into his mind that morning (though such memories, I well knew, were brought *steaming* into action like a fleet mobilised !), the recollection of my saying, years before, that I'd know all was over if ever I found myself owner of a ton of coal. Well, said my father . . . It wasn't likely that I could escape this fate now that I'd passed into the care of a young woman too sensible to agree that we should freeze. He raised a triumphant glass. 'To the happy couple—and their happy coalshed,' he said.

It was a curious pleasure of my wedding day—to see myself as my father saw me : flat on the festive floor, his foot placed with benevolent firmness on my chest.

3

Difficult to tell how *Macbeth* was going—Arnold was such a gentle producer. Later I was to see him at work in a school : he had a sort of benevolent fussiness which, combined with his smile, the tattoos on his arms, and his general appearance of a boxer suffering from a temporary attack of kindness, lifted him free of the worst disciplinary problems. If they arose, he was so incapable of real wrath that an outbreak of bad behaviour would gutter and go out, for want of fuel. If ever Arnold had kept a punishment book, it might have recorded the fashion in which he chastised this lad with a hundred smiles, and beat this other one most severely and successfully with soft, puzzled words.

As often as not, he was giving his benign attention to the actors on stage, or one or two of the actors on stage, having established no habits of discipline for the rest. I'd come from a strict dramatic background : if you were not involved for the moment, you kept most carefully quiet. All surplus actors under Arnold's regime ran about in hall or on stage, playing primitive games : talked loudly : laughed deafeningly. Arnold would sometimes direct at them the flapping hand of a man bothered, but not awfully bothered, by a fly.

It was Bing's first experience of acting. He was playing Ross, and was amazed by the way it felt. It seemed to him quite magical, this supersession of himself by an obscure Scotsman. He practised over and over again his opening words.

> The king hath happily received, Macbeth,
> The news of thy success,

at one time being overwhelmed by the thought of the different implications that could be brought about by variations of stress.

He became neurotic about it, and Broom and I had to walk him into the streets round the college and convince him that one could make a choice among all these alternatives without absolutely letting Shakespeare down.

I remembered how we'd done the play at school, the year after doing *The Importance of Being Earnest,* and how the boy who'd played Lady Bracknell played Lady Macbeth without ever really ceasing to play Lady Bracknell: and how some critical assassin in the school magazine had suggested that it was a matter of coronations not so much at Scone as at Buttered Muffin.

There were signs that our own production would have Arnold's stamp rather awfully upon it: it threatened to be the tale of the most lamentably goodnatured Macbeth (Rayner was not succeeding in being noticeably malign) and his shy Queen ('My dear, you'd never know she was in the castle!').

Kate and I were having trouble with Mrs Nape. She had no gift, at whatever busy moment, for passing you by with a nod. Any meeting converted you into an audience for one of her soliloquies. Then there was that chamber pot of hers, which was always covered with a towel, but sometimes not completely. Kate said she'd glimpsed contents that might have been produced by a small army of old ladies. We'd got into the habit of listening before using the stairs: which was where confrontations occurred, as she mounted them to visit the bathroom we shared. For a while this brought about a reduction in our meetings: but then we were back where we were—even worse—and it struck us that she, too, must have hit upon this practice of listening before leaving her part of the house. We were all listening, Kate with her shopping basket, I with my briefcase, Mrs Nape with her chamber pot. We were listening for her absence, she was listening for our presence.

There was an awful lot, now, in these soliloquies, about the late Mr Nape. He'd worked for a firm of food exporters whose name we never quite caught. It sounded absurdly like Peas and Beans. 'Yes, he was head of everything at Peas and Beans,' Mrs Nape would say. 'Old Mr Peas came to the funeral, you know. Mr Beans was long dead, of course. They worshipped my husband. Well, he gave them everything. Imagine him going on strike!' Mrs Nape imagined it, and laughed unnervingly. 'Never got home before nine o'clock. Worked himself to death.' She always sounded as though she thought this course of suicide through commercial excess was one to be proud of. 'To death'.

Kate and I arrived at the obvious conclusion about Mr Nape's late hours at the office: it caused another problem when it came, on that narrow steep stairway, to forming a sober audience for her. As she spoke of his self-destructive loyalty to Peas and Beans, we saw him in bed with the younger Miss Peas, or perhaps the elder Miss Beans: absenting himself, so to speak, from soliloquy awhile.

Another strand in these monologues was given to an account of all the people Mrs Nape knew, or faintly knew, or had once known, or had nearly known, or knew through friends: together with some she had not known, and was glad not to have known. These last had the absorbing interest of being persons who, by her account of her fortune in not knowing them, threw into relief the fineness of her actual taste in people. On the whole, the people she cared for were 'high up'. 'He used to live—oh'— she'd gasp at the thought of it—'not a mile from here—very high up in the Government, you know.' She meant he was a clerk in the Civil Service, but seemed to be just avoiding, delicately, some such statement as that he was Prime Minister. 'And she's high up in photography. She touches up, you know. Society ladies.' It sounded awfully indecent. 'No one like her, they say, for taking the wrinkles out. *Her* father's high up in the laundry business . . .'

I'd wondered sometimes how Mrs Nape spoke of us. Could she possibly make the claim that I was high up in teaching, and that Kate was high up in—well, it would have to be imminent motherhood?

Our child was now a restive matter of legs and elbows, a constant heaving and tossing in Kate's belly. She had a party trick that was capable of appalling all our parents simultaneously: a teacup standing on what passed for her lap would receive, from their clandestine grandchild, a kick that threatened to spill it.

We seemed to have been waiting for ever. *Macbeth* helped to pass the last week or so.

There was the affair of the costumes. Arnold thought he had done rather well in this matter: he'd persuaded a well-known firm to fit us out for £30. The hampers arrived, full of wooden swords, some extending only a short shattered distance beyond the hilt: helmets that seemed to have been stored in a particularly stagnant pond after some comic military Ascot: and mildewed sandals. It was the mildew on the sandals that achieved the difficult end of making Arnold angry. We took a bus, far more of us than was necessary, and confronted the costumier. He expressed surprise at our dissatisfaction—breaking, it seemed, remorseless professional oaths of secrecy to reveal to us that these very hampers had seen John Gielgud through difficult days. If we waited he would check on that, he added without moving.

Arnold had lost some of his fire and said, coaxingly, that it was because we were an educational establishment that we had to ensure the historical accuracy of any costumes we wore. The costumier failed to challenge the notion that costumes for *Macbeth* could ever be historically correct. For this reason, Arnold resumed, he thought we'd be returning the hampers— without payment, he murmured—and looking elsewhere. The costumier claimed to have heard a telephone ringing and vanished. We went, too, and along the road met another costumier, equally famous, who much enjoyed our story about the first one ('What did you expect?') and offered us genuine hampers of material suitable for *Macbeth* ('He swept that muck off the floor, you know') for £45. It would (but never mind) mean that Olivier must wait . . .

Arnold said it was an education in itself, this struggle for justice in the field of costume. It was, we gathered, to expose us to this education that he'd made his bargain with the first costumier.

Our first audience was an afternoon one, of schoolchildren. That was the term used, though it seemed hardly to describe the fiendishly cheerful swarms who, immediately the doors were opened, filled the hall much as floodwater might pour through a breach in a dam. They bore no resemblance to any audience we'd ever imagined: and the noise they made contained no promise of its replacement, in due course, by anything like attentive silence. Indeed, talk of floodwater hardly covers the case.

It was as if several oceans had chosen to pour their waters on a single beach.

'Surely,' said Arnold nervously, 'they have teachers with them?'

Rayner had been out in front. 'The teachers seem to have gone for a walk,' he said. This turned out to be largely true: they obviously took it that a performance in a teachers' training college hardly needed patrolling. Though Bing insisted that, given the character of the audience, it was at least as likely that some teachers had simply been bound and gagged and tossed under the seats.

The curtain up, it was evident that we were not in the presence of experienced playgoers. The mere spectacle of the witches, half-visible through flame and smoke, was regarded, by a substantial section of the audience, as an outrage. Individual cries of protest could be heard above the general din. 'Who are they supposed to be?' 'Fire! Help! *Fire!*' As the witches crept out of back-stage obscurity and offered themselves to the footlights, the mood changed to one of extremely wild amusement. There seemed to be a lot of falling about, together with attempts to keep laughter within bounds by punching one's neighbour in the ribs. Against Arnold's advice, all three witches had elected to speak in quavering falsetto. The audience was loudly inclined to attribute this to physical misadventure.

It was, I'm afraid, an introduction to teacherly casualness. There can have been little attempt to prepare the children for the play. They projected their disbelief horrifically at every change of scene, at the entry of every character. The slaughter of Lady Macduff and her son was received as pure farce. Marvellous stabbing and screaming! Macbeth, who'd worked up a decent head of murderous steam in final rehearsals, was quite demoralised by the experience, and began to quaver and insert hesitations into his speeches so that it all rapidly declined into what must have been the only portrayal of the tyrant as a nervously bothered man with a tendency, at moments of crisis, to inaudibility. Some of us found it impossible not to laugh. It happened for me in the scene of my murder, when I discovered that the murderers had doubled in number: two small boys had climbed on to the stage and were—but with a sort of puzzled politeness—advancing towards me in the company of the official assassins.

The only triumph of the afternoon was, quite unexpectedly, Miss Longbone's. She may have been mild, but her years of teaching paid off as she fed into her impersonation of Lady Macbeth the genuine ire of a sixth form teacher faced with— well, perhaps a rebellious congress of fourth forms. This was Lady Macbeth as an outraged long-established member of a grammar school staff, and it was, in the strange context, quite magnificent. Miss Longbone's concession to the occasion was to omit that detailed invitation to the forces of evil to come to her woman's breasts, and so forth. It was only too likely to have been taken up by some of this audience.

In the end it seemed that audience and performers had become totally separate groups, both foolishly attempting to conduct unconnected riots in the same small space. It was a deeply, hilariously horrifying experience, and left us ready for the most dreadful failure on the first night.

Arnold's despair was tremendous. 'If it's not four million times better than this,' he cried, with the air of someone quoting sober statistics, 'it will be the most awful failure known to man.' The idea of winning such a dreadful place in history appealed to no one. But when it came to it, some such multiplication of quality must have taken place. It was a wild success. Rayner in the title role was suddenly very good. Miss Longbone, without ever ceasing to suggest that she would much rather not make all this fuss, was firm : a little diabolical : and really very moving indeed in the sleepwalking scene. Of Perring it could be said that on the night he promoted Duncan from constable to inspector : a great improvement. As so often happens, the English scene caused general tears—largely because of the quality of the Macduff : who said that the play had done more than anything to lay, for him, some terrible wartime ghosts.

As Bing said, it was the author who was primarily responsible for the transformation of the ragged production we knew from rehearsal to this performance in which the many flaws were out-weighed by the great intentness—even earnestness—of the acting. Bing was astonished by what the mere attentiveness of an audience could do for you. 'Like giving us a beautifully clean piece of paper to draw on,' he said. Rayner said that, for some reason, he waited every night, with a sort of longing, to say :

> Be innocent of the knowledge, dearest chuck,
> Till thou applaud the deed.

Those words, he said, were a total pleasure to speak.

Even Rumble shared in the general awe and strange delight felt by the cast—though he did not allow it to prevent him from asking everyone, from Mr Trellis downwards, to give him a frank opinion of his characterisation of Young Siward. It was, he said, perhaps particularly important that people should be honest with him. Others in the cast, who had been acting Shakespeare as long as they could remember—born with theatrical silver spoons in their mouths—were so hardened to criticism that they could be forgiven for not understanding that someone like him had to grow accustomed to praise.

Or, of course, to blame.

Mr Jepp was inspired, though it's not perhaps quite the word, to discuss, in a main course lecture, the role of the ghosts, witches and other apparitions in the play as a sort of visual aid to the supernatural. He hoped sniggerers at the back would allow him to describe Banquo's ghost as epidiascopic. And students who were not total idiots, and the half dozen students concerned would know who he meant, must have been struck by the thought that the procession of royal figures that appear to Macbeth amounted to an unnerving forerunner of the film strip.

4

Kate leaned against my knee and we listened to Segovia on the radio. Music had provided a meeting place for our separately rambling emotions, so often. There'd been an evening when we were listening to Brahms's Alto Rhapsody—Kathleen Ferrier the singer. Towards the end, her voice coming, so tall and pure, out of the dark rustle of men's voices : rising and gathering to itself the jubilant melancholy of the whole work, setting itself free from that long sweet dragging and shuffling, and we'd together burst into tears. Now we heard the thin clarity of this playing of Segovia's, the hesitation at the peak of a melody, the tumbling down then into a valley of sound composed of more notes than it seemed a single hand could manage. And so to bed.

And Kate wet. Was it blood? We turned on a fearful light. It was water. Her water bag had burst. I was to rush to the phone next door and report this event to the hospital.

Mrs Nape at her bedroom door as I scuttled down the stairs. 'Kate's water bag . . .' Had Kate got the phrase right? Could it be a *water bag*? I expected the hospital to ask for a clinical expansion of the term—for details and assurances I couldn't offer. But they simply said an ambulance would be coming.

Somehow the old lady from next door was in the hall. 'A dry birth,' I heard Mrs Nape murmuring, with dramatic satisfaction. Kate was dressing—shivering as she did so. 'They're sending a lorry.'

'Oh—oh, I don't think I can bear any jokes.'

'They're sending an ambulance, at once.'

I was walking, in no time, through the empty night streets, with Kate's clothes in a little bag. I was knocking at my parents' door, asking for a night's lodging. They fussed, to my entire satisfaction. It was agreeable to be surrounded by tremulous fussing.

My father remembered his teeth were out. Mother's were out, too. Suddenly enormously old, they fussed me to a spare bed, and I fell asleep while composing a host of incompatible scenarios. 'A dry birth' was the phrase I fell asleep with, imagining our child, withered like a neglected plant. Enormously *young*—and dry.

At Isleden, the next day, Mr Jepp seemed to lecture on education and childbirth: Mr Salt to collect our opinions on *Moll Flanders* and the mysterious disappearance of my wife, Kate. I had become an aching emptiness, was altogether in abeyance. I rang the hospital and they said, each time: 'No change.' I felt as I'd felt only once before, on our wedding day—that curious sensation of being different from everyone else in the world. I urged haste on my imminent, unknown child. I ordered myself sternly to remember that birth was not the least common of events, and to behave casually. 'I shouldn't,' said Bing, catching me at it. 'You'll burst.'

Near to midnight I learned that we had this son, who would probably be called Tom.

I felt I'd been separated from Kate for aeons. My imagination ached with inventing our reunion. And part of me winced away from my own excitement. My companions must really be smiling to themselves. So commonplace, a birth! This commonplace, unique event!

As white as the hospital nightshirt she wore, open down the front. Suddenly very thin, very hot, scrubbed colourless, a sort of reproductive maid-of-all-work, and never more beautiful. 'How are you?' I asked, with helpless inadequacy, and she pointed to the crib at the side of the bed. In it, a sleeping stranger, with a large bruise on his temple. Kate began to cry. 'Oh, I don't really want to do this,' she said, and her tears became more urgent. There was the memory of terror in them. He'd been twisted—head nowhere, arms and legs everywhere. Faithfully Kate had obeyed instructions, but to no effect. There'd been impatience—the problem slowly understood. Then anaesthesia, forceps.

'I was so rowdy,' said Kate. 'I could hear them shouting above my screams. I apologised to the doctor this morning.'

She'd thought, in the violence of it, that the baby was dead. She'd thought it had all come to nothing.

He'd been battered round the boxing ring of birth all right. Such bruises. And such an agreeable face. He'd come, exceedingly pleasant, out of the screaming and the groping with forceps, and was safely asleep. My senses swam as I looked at him, with a feeling of the paradox of his existence. No one could ever be closer. No one could ever be more unfamiliar. Such a fusion of the utterly known, the totally unknown.

Such an intimate stranger . . .

5

I was being converted, I thought, into an uneasily numerate
St John's ambulance man with an hysterical approach to the use
of the epidiascope and a pathetic acquaintance with papier
mâché.

The element of St John's Ambulance was introduced by Mr
Potton. He was a man given to a sort of vague briskness. Fundamentally a gymnast, he was small and neat of frame, and bounced
rather than walked. He always carried a folder or a briefcase, as
if to convince others—and perhaps himself—of his awareness
that paperwork and intellectual organisation were vital aspects
of his task as a lecturer. In fact, paper confused him enormously.
Ideas, words, timetables—everything baffled him but varieties of
bouncing. One tried to keep paper out of one's contact with
him. Let him unhappily begin to ruffle through the contents of a
folder, and chaos was come.

'You're Smith.' You weren't. 'Let me see, I have your essay
somewhere.' He hadn't. 'I remember it quite well. It was on Diet
in the Primary School.' It wasn't. You hadn't given him an essay.
You'd intended to ask him, indeed, if it was true that he had set
an essay on The Schoolchild and His Teeth : and if that was not
a mistake, since during those strange, stammered occasions that
formed his course on Health and Hygiene, he had skipped from
Hair to Digestion with no reference at all to intermediate areas.

'Don't say I can't find it.' You didn't say so; and in addition
you were unwilling now to disclose your real purpose in accosting
him. Experience told you that it was best to let him exhaust his
own wild line of inquiry. 'But it was a reasonable essay. I
remember that. Does B minus seem about right?' You sighed.
'The trouble is, there are so many Smiths in the college.' Somewhere about this point, he would drop his folder. You would

97

both be standing ankle-deep in paper. 'I think you'd better see me after the lecture this afternoon.'

There was no lecture that afternoon.

I found it always a relief to be with Mr Salt. He did not merely have a need to rub himself against walls : he was compelled also to cling to doorknobs. There was always, as with gentle intentness he burrowed for our benefit into his thoughts, this curious impression as of a man who'd be swept away if he didn't cling, rub, generally writhe. It had been discussed in hall—not Mr Salt's habits in particular, but the general question of our all having them, and as teachers being very likely to cultivate grotesque variations on them : and the need, as it were, to prune now and then some of the wilder growths. Mr Jepp was strong on this, but less impressive than he might have been—his plea for careful colourlessness in the classroom being underlined with such optical detonations and throwing up of arms, with the accompanying loss of stitches and buttons. In a bad moment Mr Jepp, who could be cruel, had seized on the wearing of yellow socks and brilliant blue velvet suits by the secretary of the college literary society as the absolute example of unwise dress. As bad in the classroom, he said, as picking your nose or banging your head against the wall. His victim continued to wear what in those days was regarded as gaudy costume. Catching sight of him during a lecture, or in a corridor, Mr Jepp would stop, glare and inflict further ruin on his own suit, which, theoretically respectable in its herringbone or pinstriped gloom, in fact hung about him like an oath.

But Mr Salt was altogether an awkward man, physically. At times he would seem to be suffering from sudden, very severe knee damage, and would stumble about the room, flexing his leg over and over again. His gestures were all very odd, as though under his country tweeds he was made of wood, and all the joints had been wrongly constructed : so that his limbs never quite moved in expected directions. But it all seemed part of what was so valuable in him : the intent firsthandness he brought to everything.

I had no doubt that if I was going to be a teacher, I wanted to be as much as possible like Mr Salt. I was already beginning to see that a teacher can only construct himself slowly out of his own characteristics . . . which sounds obvious, until you measure

98

the difficulty of being in any respect yourself in a classroom. You couldn't become a teacher of Mr Salt's order through imitation. But in a setting where so many attempts were made to catch the essence of teaching in this or that mechanical way, in some formula—some rule about socks—it was of enormous value to meet someone who offered glimpses of that essence as it truly is : so much more mysterious than the most sensible rule or formula or adjuration could ever suggest.

He told us at times, hands clumsily twisting, of his childhood and youth, in the country, and the longing, and the love of people and poetry, that had driven him into teaching. The language in which he spoke of these things had a certain awkwardness about it, too, except that this lay in some kind of old-fashionedness : it was a rounded, slightly solemn speech, full of nineteenth century echoes, and stuffed with allusions to verse. He talked, in fact, bookishly : but it was a bookishness that had learned to be at the service of an exceedingly efficient teacher—and latterly, we'd gathered from several sources, a marvellous headmaster. It was, you might have said, a sort of plain-dealing orotundity.

The fact is that Mr Salt was in love with teaching. It was a lifelong romantic assignation with an occupation. There was even a time, he said, when he'd felt uncomfortable about being paid for it . . . . having been allowed, as he put it, to teach nothing but English and Art. English and Art all week long! Could we imagine the delight of it?

He read to us a great deal, much poetry. He thought the only thing to do about poetry was to read it at odd moments, to quote it on any natural occasion, to convey generally the idea that poetry had a perfectly ordinary workaday part to play in any-one's life. Indeed, the point of it all might be to suggest how human beings could acquire one of the most important bridges they needed : a readily useable connection between the ordinary and the extraordinary, with traffic running both ways.

He read us a poem of de la Mare's at the end of a tutorial and the last line coincided with the end of the period. We rose to go. Mr Salt was apologetic. How bad of him, to leave no silence after the reading. 'I would try to time it, in a classroom, so that nothing had to be said—we would have our little, but distinct, silence, and then the children would go away with the poem in their minds.' Mr Salt surrendered the doorknob to Capper, who was aware of P.E.-time running to waste. 'Two days later we might want to talk about it like mad.'

When we discoursed or read papers he remained calm through the most awful gaffes and insensitivities, only now and then having to cling specially hard to some fixture or fitting. It happened once in Op Lit when Trimmer was mumbling through a disquisition on *The Way of All Flesh*. Trimmer's hatred of religious inquiry, which so oddly had taken him into the anti-R.I. group, had recently branched out, there, into hatred of philosophy. Philosophers, he'd grumbled, were largely to blame for human misery: it being their profession to loll about (his phrase) and think up painful problems: past which, without their interference, men might have succeeded in tiptoeing. Of literature he had a view with much the same roots. Literature also tended to stir things up, to be an elaborate exercise in failing to leave well alone. Now he was giving his attention to this vexatious novel of Samuel Butler's, one of the worst examples he'd encountered, and was led into a comment on the plight of Victorian women. They had hardly any education, he grumbled: as though this were not a condition that met most of his own objections to the way the world conducted itself. 'All they learned,' he declared, 'was needlework, and music, with only a few volumes of Byron to stimulate their imaginations.'

Mr Salt clung with both hands to a window-fastening and wedged his toes under a desk.

'That last was pretty potent,' he said.

6

The anti-R.I. group, indeed, was dwindling. A feeling had grown up that, in a general atmosphere in which we seemed to be having letters tied round our necks, it might lead to our leaving college a declared D, a denounced E.

Mr Jepp dropped in on the group and said he used the religious element in assembly quite frankly to establish the tone of his school, to assert its solidarity. Accordingly, he preferred hymns to be as meaningless as possible. Nonsense hymns would suit him very well. He glared at us genially, a sort of cloven-footed saint.

Bing murmured that such hymns were not difficult to find. But wasn't it dangerous, he protested, to use irrational instruments to create an atmosphere? Mr Jepp's eyes crackled and smoked, but before he could reply Mr Trellis uttered a string of soft chuckles and said, Well, we were irrational anyway. Agreed, said Bing, but we *tried* to be rational: we avoided being *deliberately* irrational. Mr Trellis chuckled again, with that effect of tolerant wisdom that sometimes made the whole college wish to shake him: and Mr Jepp growled into his moustache.

It reminded me of my father, and of what had happened when my friend, Roger Bunce, had turned up and blundered into some reference to christening. We'd be starting Tom off on the right foot, he supposed, staring down at our son as, quite clearly a long way from being on any kind of foot, he leaned back in Kate's arms. Not long before he'd been singing like a nestful of birds: but now, with his supercilious after-dinner face, and hands crossed on his breast, he looked for all the world like some very much reduced bishop.

My friendship with Roger Bunce had dated from our earliest days in the grammar school. He was given then to buying sweets and keeping them to himself. But he didn't eat them secretly; he'd take them out with a kind of private openness, and consume them in a very busy, concentrated fashion. He'd stare into the bag, sometimes at great length, before deciding on his next mouthful. I remember not knowing how to speak of this, and having my first important experience of the distress of being compelled to bottle up indignation and a sense of injustice. There were times when I expected Roger to be struck down by some supernatural agency for such an infringement of the schoolboys' code. As time went on, this perfectly calm habit of keeping things to himself showed up in other departments. It was not, in any conventional sense, selfishness. It was . . . a constitutional unwillingness, I think, ever to journey far from his own centre. As a stores clerk in the Army, he'd been stationed all over the warring world; but he'd always taken with him what I thought of as a very tiny country, Bunceland. In letters from abroad, he related his encounters with exotic persons. An Arab straight out of the desert: an Indian from some cranny in that northwestern frontier, bristling with knives, a walking museum of old guns: this lovely girl from the Caribbean, wearing largely what Roger identified as a sort of raffia. Entering Roger's presence, what use was their exotic character to any of them? The poetry fell away and left them total prose. Roger had enrolled them at once as citizens in his own drab republic. And, I guess, he did not share his sweets with any of them . . .

Indeed, as I used to complain, Roger needed to knock the strangeness out of any place, idea or event before he could begin to enjoy it. Through the years I'd been made furious, at times, by his systematic low temperature. He, in his turn, was irritated by my loose and sometimes ecstatic vagueness. It had been like that as we shuffled through the town, absentees from games, on far-off Wednesday afternoons. I'd phrase once more the idea I had that there was no point, at least at this stage, in settling for less than a life of glory and immense fame. Roger would say: 'Oh really, you're all gas and noise. Calm down, man. You'll see—you'll settle to being an ordinary chap like the rest of us.' To which I'd howl my reply: 'I have no intention of being ordinary! What a thing to say! *What* a thing to say in an amazing world like this, full of Mozarts and Greta Garbos and Van Goghs and . . .' And some such string of my current heroes. And Roger, the efficient fireman of these exchanges, would bring his hoses to bear again: 'You're going to break a blood vessel one day, you ass!'

There was cruelty, I knew, in my feelings towards him and in his towards me. It had always been there, since we were small, a need to bite and hurt because he knew I thought him prosaic and scandalously unexcitable, and I knew he thought me ridiculously airy and pretentious. But I leaned on him a great deal, on the very limitations that made me angry. When I was giddily miserable and dismayed, I could always recover in the flat air of Bunceland. And in me he had, I think, the fireman's delight in a blazing house. He liked persuading himself that he was putting my flames out.

Now, once more an insurance clerk, he'd dropped in to gaze at

Tom, at a moment when all the grandparents were present. And he'd made this remark about christening. But there would be no christening, I said, and there was an incredulous cry from Kate's mother, as if I'd said we were donating our son to the gypsies : and my father said, 'That's all right'—(which on his lips meant that things had gone very wrong)—'let them alone'—(always uttered as though only my father's weary tolerance stood between the offender in question and a lynching)—'they'll fall into the old-fashioned ways in due course.'

7

First there'd be Christmas, and then the beginning of the ridiculous year 1950, a date out of the science fiction of my childhood : then second teaching practice. Meanwhile, we were deep into the combined course : defined as an introduction to experiences in local studies and science, light arts and crafts. I couldn't imagine in what sense the word 'light' was used . . .

But this was to assume that there would be a Christmas, a New Year, a world fit for arts and crafts of any weight whatever.

'What a terrible world it is,' said Ben, 'when you can't think about what's happening without going mad.'

There was this feeling, so strong then, of the double future. There were the years ahead for which you planned, or the expectation of which made sense of present action. There was having a child, a conventional investment in the idea of a normal future. At the same time, there was the totally opposite, and also very strong, anticipation that everything would soon, and hideously, come to an end. In my diary, that autumn, I find I'd written : 'How odd, it sometimes seems, to keep this record, when it appears so likely that in a year's time it will be so much charred paper'.

The educational attaché from the Soviet Embassy came to talk to us about Soviet schooling. Or rather, with some excuse about his English being uncertain, he read us a long report on perfection. He seemed very young, and I thought how strange it was that one looked on a Russian as a visitor from some remote planet.

At times, especially in the presence of my tiny son, I'd wonder what it would be like to live otherwise than under the black weather of our international madness. There he'd be, a faint mess of dried milk on cheeks and chin. His face restless with the flickering of very small, very obscure annoyances: his mouth constantly in action, working away, at suckling practice perhaps. As to that, Kate had observed on a recent occasion that he looked exactly like my father at the moment when he took his first sip of a pint of beer: and had actually blushed. Feeding had altogether turned out more complex than she'd imagined. There had to be a finger holding his nose clear, and another ensuring that his tongue was under and not over the nipple, and yet another tapping his cheek to keep him awake. Two sucks and he was unconscious, if you didn't watch him. There'd been a technical surprise, too—the discovery that the milk came out, not in a central jet but in a spray. 'I've become a sort of watering can,' Kate had explained, rather defensively.

While still in hospital she'd written to explain the vast amount of weeping that had accompanied her early jubilation. 'We have experienced a great happiness in bringing Tom into the world, but this is mixed with an intolerable, sad uncertainty as to what the future holds for him. There is only one consolation in the case of war—our share of the horror will be as great as his own—'

I'd had a seizure of despair about this time, brought on by the collision between the experience of a birth and the pervasive idea of monstrous destruction: and had written to Ben. In favour, as always, of staying alive and sane, he'd replied calmingly:

'You and I (and Kate and Marie too) are really only just growing up. We have all four of us some idea—some vision if you like—of things as they ought to be. What we all lack, and are currently acquiring, is a grasp of things and people as they are. Later, perhaps very much later, we shall get a proper balance between the two. Then we shall be poised, easy and serene (if the earth remains patiently beneath our feet), you will be a good teacher, I a benign bureaucrat . . . Until then we need not really be ashamed of our defects along the way.

'More immediately and practically a little pragmatism helps me. It should help you too. We cannot cure society overnight. We should destroy ourselves if we tried. But we can present as much of ourselves to the problem in hand as seems healthy.'

We'd tried to do that a couple of years before : that is, we'd formed a Fabian group. We'd met once or twice at home, and my father had been curiously jolly about having a gang of socialists, however mild, conferring in his sitting room. It was the room we rarely used, the one with the piano and the fat chairs and the clock that chimed spectacularly without ever actually keeping time. My father said he didn't mind, at all, but he would reserve the right, when sending in coffee, to tie the spoon to the tray. I realised then that he liked the outrageousness of it, and having his house used, and being able to be accidentally in the hall during arrivals and departures, representing, as he saw it, ordinary decency and common sense. He enjoyed coming in with a spray after they'd all gone and fumigating the room. It gave him great pleasure to pretend that he thought Maurice, a pervasively bearded Frenchman who'd recently joined us, was Karl Marx himself. He emptied the ash trays as if he'd been a bomb disposal squad, and was delighted to come across a crumpled note of mine roughing out the title for a pamphlet : 'The position of Fabian Socialism in modern left-wing confusion.'

Ben at a second attempt had just broken his way into the administrative class of the Civil Service : and my father, now as a civil servant left behind, was furious to hear of this. The suggestion was that Ben's superiors had confused him with someone else. '£850 a year, at his age ! I hope young Fletcher knows how lucky he is !' My father never called my friends by their Christian names : and of all of them he used the word 'young' with interesting bitterness. On his lips, it was a terrible word. It had always been 'young fellows' who had overtaken him. 'I hope he's not expecting to get very much further. £850 a year ! Phew !' It was as if he were commenting on the career of some sort of bureaucratic harlot.

However, as he said, he saw the funny side of it, having this young fellow, appallingly overpaid, sitting in the drawing room, propounding radical change. 'But you won't have him long, you know! All right being a socialist on £400 a year! Now they've given him £850 he'll soon see the beauties of capitalism!'

He tended to lag far behind events. So Roger Bunce, by my father's standards politically spotless, was held to be 'another of your young bolsheviks' on the strength of a brief episode over ten years old. We were in the sixth form at the time. Actually I was then writing a series of poems, something of the tone of them taken from Yeats, blameless Yeats, and marked by a fashionable failure of rhyme. At the time, the idea of not quite rhyming filled me with awful excitement. Yeats was one of my victims, and Roger was another, for he was the hero of the series.

> Along the city street there passes
> One of many tight untender faces,
> Rapt upon its minute purpose,
> Crawling across the clock's face.
> This is Roger who foretold
> The regeneration of the world.

Hard on Roger, very. There were many moments when you'd have said of his face that it was loose and fairly fond. He could be untender, of course, when I was throwing my poetic weight about—but I deserved that. And then he'd had only that very short period of utopianism, of a very sober kind. It had struck him for a few months, as it might momentarily strike anyone, however generally immune to bold ideas, that, by this or that rearrangement, the world might be made a better place. It was Bunceism, very remote from Marxism, rather cooler than Fabianism. It was the vaguest socialism warming up over the merest glimmer of gas. It hadn't taken Roger long to turn the tap off altogether and to evolve the more characteristic political theory that an attempt to change almost anything was the first step on a road that would end with the sacking of Buckingham Palace.

But still, all these years later, Roger to my fascinated father was one of your young bolsheviks: though heading for rehabilitation, of course, when his salary had reached that level that made ordinary decency and common sense inevitable.

It was the reason why my father had this almost indiscernible enthusiasm for my being a teacher. He couldn't see it ever offering me such a salary as would, so to speak, winch me out of the bog of bolshevism.

Jack Hagger, chairing our encounter with the Soviet attaché, said during the vote of thanks that he hoped the visitor's address would answer some of the questions we'd brought with us from teaching practice. Only that morning someone, in a tutorial, had wanted to know what to do about a boy who came behind him calling out ghastly names, but was never there when he turned. How difficult for anyone from the Soviet Union or the republics of Eastern Europe to begin to understand such problems! There, self-discipline prevailed, reflecting a similar joyous condition in the society outside the school.

Jack's ardour was so generous, his belief in these great transformations so entire, that no one really knew how to contradict him. It would have been like heckling the Brothers Grimm.

Questions about that first teaching practice had come out late, like bruises. I was left with one or two, difficult to deal with—dilemmas and uncertainties with the quality of rolls of barbed wire.

There was puzzlement, for example, as between the idea of the joy it should be to teach, and some wretched realities. I'd liked so many of the boys at Eastbourne Road; but oh, how miserably equipped they were, in dress and speech and mind and experience. And what a gulf between the top boy with his body supple with his sense of brightness, and the bottom one, knotted and frowning with his sense of dullness!

Was I hard enough to enter this most nerve-racking occupation at this level?

And, absurdly, what about the connection between education and inedibility? At Eastbourne Road the school dinners that had not tasted generally of sherbet had tasted generally of pyorrhoea. I'd struggled for a long time to categorise the taste of Isleden dinners, and concluded that it was that of . . . London fog.

If one's wits were strong enough for teaching, was one's stomach?

8

It was strange to have a third with us, an almost non-social third. Tom's presence among us was so odd, being entirely unlike that of any kind of companion we'd ever known. He was not a baby in the sense in which, before he arrived, we'd imagined a baby. To begin with, he was a source of extraordinary noises. The nights were filled with esoteric gruntings and whistlings. Sometimes he sounded like a whole wainscot-full of mice. Then he'd belch, or fart—and about that there was something incongruously adult. We'd flush a little—there being an element of parody and satire in it.

He'd sit sometimes on the enormous lap of Kate's grandmother, and there were only four or five years short of a century between them.

The old lady had been living with Kate's parents for years. It was difficult, for she went on to be 101, and they were not free until they'd lost the habit of it. Tiny, square, she looked always as if she were standing to attention : which, exactly like a soldier, she always did when being photographed. She had what appeared to be expectations of immortality : at any rate, was known to be saving money so that she could look after herself when her daughter and son-in-law were gone. But this was part of a general habit of thrift. She had never reconciled herself to the practice—necessarily limited in Kate's family, which was never well-off—of buying a new dress, a new pair of shoes, when there was still a dress with life in it, still a pair of shoes not worn out. Her most remarkable parsimony was in respect of the Christmas presents she received : which she put aside and, next year, recycled. Kate's mother would nervously intervene, from time to time, to prevent the ultimate mishap from occurring : the returning of a present to its original donor. But Kate's

108

mother had little authority over granny, who treated her always like a child.

She'd been in service as a girl in London, and then had married a gardener, in a village on the Thames, where Kate was born. They had a tiny house full of exquisite smells, of soaps and fresh ironing and apples and lavender and dried herbs—smells, that, encountered anywhere, would make Kate cry out with nostalgic delight. It was set, the house, in what Kate remembered as an infinitely large garden, a specimen of her grandfather's skill, lawns and an orchard and, in the season, raspberry canes trained like tents, inside which Kate, with cousins, would sit scrumping. There was croquet and, somewhere in the village, tennis, and photos showed Kate's mother, in some summer before the First World War, decorous and trim in the tennis dress of the time, with her partner, who won tournaments with her but did not win her. She threw him over for Kate's father, brought wounded from France to mend in the village. He was a saddler's son, so country wed country.

Kate's grandfather appears in many of those photos : usually, in that summer garden, being handed a cup of tea by his wife : she with ballooning shoulders and vast dousing hats, he a solid packet of tweed. Even his face was clothed, in a tremendous beard of wicked cut, not quite square, a twist in it somewhere as there was in his devilish eyebrows. A man, said Kate, with something strange and uncommon hidden inside him, which he perhaps used up in his care of gardens, in his famous flair for roses.

He'd given her, once, actually in a woodshed, the sort of shock that is supposed to unhinge : but in her case failed of that effect. She came across him piddling on the coal, kept in a corner of the shed. It was quite a hosing he was giving it, she said. Later, she discovered that he always did this, on some perfectly practical principle : it laid the dust, he held. Kate didn't get away scotfree, though the lifelong result was a jolly one : the shed was always kept pungently creosoted, and that smell, encountered anywhere and at any time, made her feel instantly, and not disagreeably, wicked . . .

Kate and her grandmother had a skirmishing affection for each other. Little that Kate did met with approval. Her going out with young men in motorcars was vice unvarnished. Her coming in late at night was the end of maidenly modesty everywhere. Worst of all was her underwear. It wasn't so much the moral aspect of its skimpiness as the medical aspect. It invited prompt pneumonia and death. Granny grumbling over the ironing was a feature of life in Kate's home.

She was polite to me, but I knew she thought little of me. Not the solid fellow with a practical occupation she'd have wished for. On occasions after marriage when we stayed with Kate's parents, she'd find herself ironing my underwear, and then her regret was clinched. These weren't the garments of a man who'd bring Kate to her senses. Granny's reaction was that of someone bracing herself for a funeral no later than next week. 'How can he expect to get through the winter dressed like this. Eh, Dolly?' And Kate's mother, who had much trouble in dealing with granny's stentorian whispers, would cry: 'Ssh!' The house had thin walls, and I was in the next room. 'What's that? What do you say, Dolly?' 'I said shh!' 'I don't see why they bother to wear anything,' granny would roar, confidentially.

There was something about the obstinate ancient smallness of her that made me feel she was towering above me. I wanted sometimes, when I found her dissatisfied eye upon me, to spring to my feet and salute, with the greatest respect.

It was a fading eye. She had a passion for detective novels, and until her mid-nineties read them till late at night. I noticed that as her sight vanished, she turned the resulting failure to read into a virtue. So, when Bertrand Russell's Reith lectures were published in *The Listener*, she threw a copy aside with a cry of: 'Nothing new!' My having literary pretensions, coupled with the inadequacy of my underclothes, made her come down quite harshly on men of letters. So it was when Bernard Shaw died. 'I see you've lost the founder of the Fabians,' she said, as if it were a case of carelessness on my part. 'No drinking, no smoking, and no religion. Clever head for writing, but not for the main thing! Pity!' she exclaimed, shuffling off to do some more censorious ironing. 'A man like that could have done a lot of good!'

There were times when I longed to bring granny together with Mr Trellis, or confidently to pit her failing eye against Mr Jepp's eruptive one.

9

A letter appeared in the *New Statesman* from a graduate teacher, alleging that 'retired gentlefolk' could teach as well as emergency trainees, who were not worth more than £300 a year.

On the morning this appeared, Capper sat at the back of the hall, during an R.I. lecture, attempting to weld together a reply. As the experience with his thesis had shown, literary labour to Capper was very much a branch of heavy industry : one had a sense of furnaces roaring, the clatter of large machinery, immense bangs and hisses and a general atmosphere of strong language. On this occasion, said eyewitnesses (and, it being Capper, ear-witnesses too), the main hall lecture quite lost its official centre, on the platform, where Mr Dash was doing gentle things with a flannelgraph, and became centred on Capper, clangorously at work on his letter to *The Times*. At intervals he would inquire, in a great growl, why that silly bugger didn't shut up . . . Bing suggested afterwards that we should get together to write a letter, with some hope of publication, and sign it with Capper's name, so that one of the most extraordinary events in the history of minor literature might be brought about : the appearance in *The Times* of a letter by our explosively inarticulate friend. But nothing came of it.

This was one of the sillier attacks on the emergency course. Most were based on a fairly vulgar calculation : that thirteen months training must be less effective than two years. It was all reach-me-down, hurried, shallow. The most odious opponent of the scheme I encountered was an elderly teacher on the staff of my second practice school. 'If you don't mind my saying so,' he said, 'you emergency trained teachers are not well read enough. You have to become omnivorous readers. *Omnivorous!*' I expected him to test my understanding of the word with a quick question. I wasn't ready then with the reply I could have offered five years later: that emergency trainees were as likely to have raised as lowered the level of literacy in a profession less noted for readers accustomed to devouring everything than for readers inclined to devour nothing.

Ben had read the letter in the *New Statesman* with scorn. He was now working, he said, among men who'd all come into the Civil Service from the university. He'd expected them to be, in some subtle but unmistakable way, superior to him, who'd joined the service at eighteen from the grammar school. But, uncomfortably, he found many of them rather less bright than himself. Yes, he did feel it as a discomfort: because it brought home to him that he'd been relying on some awfully over-simple model of the incidence of human brilliance. In fact, he was wondering now if at the highest public levels men and women were always as remarkable as he'd assumed they were. 'Of course, I'd always guessed there were fools at the top. But I thought they were clever fools. Now I see that they might simply be mediocre fools. Is it the same in education, do you think?'

But the experience I was going through had riveted my attention on my own folly. I limited my answer to a grin.

'I expect, for all your modesty, that you're setting the educational Thames on fire, here and there,' said Ben, with amazing inaccuracy.

It seemed to tie in with these matters when, a few days later, Mr Salt introduced us to the term 'multilateral'. It meant, it seemed, that you put everyone into a single school: it would be rather like the railway lines coming into Euston—there would be departures and arrivals in and from all directions, but under one livery, with a single terminus in which all would start and finish side by side. It meant the station . . . the nation wouldn't be divided in two at the age of eleven. It seemed an exciting idea.

Another word for it, said Mr Salt doubtfully, was 'comprehensive'.

If I was to set the educational Thames on fire, it would be— but it quite plainly wouldn't be—at Seven Elms, I learned. It was one of those suburbs grown out of villages: in this case, grown out of the presence, presumably, of seven elm trees. A more suitable name for it in the early weeks of 1950, when I first saw it, would have been Dozens and Dozens of Shoeshops. There was, all along the High Street and along streets leading off it, this obsession with footwear.

Barnacre Secondary looked like a bungalow gone mad. From the entrance and assembly halls it thrust out single-storey arms in all directions: pink-bricked, pink-tiled, they gave the impression of trying desperately to get away from each other. It really was all limbs, and this deprived the school of any feeling of wholeness. Inside, it was endless corridors, from which, as you trudged along them, you looked out across grass to other arms and legs that were also endless corridors.

I'd been warned by a student who'd been there on his first practice that it was a devil of a school; with an uncooperative staff, a generally listless way of life. The Head was a bully, who'd told my informant: 'I'm not going to be a bloody wet-nurse to you.' The supervising tutor said it was the one school in the district he disliked. He was sorry it had to be used: but the emergency scheme had multiplied by three the number of schools needed for teaching practice. He had told Mr Trellis that if anyone went there again, he'd have to be good.

That couldn't, I thought, be the principle on which I'd been chosen. I was inclined, like most students, to imagine Mr Jepp and Mr Trellis laughing cruelly as they threw dice . . .

The weather seemed appropriately mean as I approached Barnacre for the first time, to introduce myself and arrange an opening week's programme. Big doleful clouds, miserable little winds of that spiteful kind that, when you've adjusted to their coming from one quarter, instantly come from another. Already I was beginning to realise that you could tell much about a school from the simple act of entering it. This felt cold, unenergetic. The Head was absent, ill, and his deputy was a slow, dull man, who took ages to master the mere fact of my arrival. 'You're a student, then—from Isleden?' he asked, when I'd been there long enough to qualify as some sort of intimate. He took me to the staffroom, a frosty place. With the impatient aid of men who seemed reluctant to tear themselves away from crossword puzzles, I pieced together a week's teaching. I went then to say goodbye to the deputy, who recognised me at once as a publisher's representative. They'd spent that year's requisition and more, he said. Good afternoon.

I left it at that.

I had, before teaching practice began, an experience with my son that revived in me a basic doubt about my intended profession.

We had not yet grown used to being woken every morning by the operations of a steel factory working under pressure. Some of the larger cogs in the vast machinery of the place needed oiling; they squealed supernally. There was an accident in Number Nine Vat, if that was the word for it, and molten metal ran about the floor, spitting. A hooter, its damping mechanism broken, called a shift into action, and another out of it. Hundreds of workmen tramped in various directions. They all went on strike and cheered the leaders. Someone ran among them, tickling them under the armpits, and they giggled, three or four thousand of them by now, a mass giggle somewhere above top C. It led, as my father always averred such amusement would, to tears. Now eight thousand strong, they wept. They howled. Sorrow had never been so loud.

You woke and traced the bedlam to this tiny, recently acquired son lying in a corner of the room. You hurried to take him into your own bed. He was at once totally pacified. You unwrapped him and he re-discovered arms and hands, and gave them their furious freedom.

And one morning you stuck your tongue out at him and smiled: and a responsive smile very slowly unfolded, beginning in his eyes, catching his lips, dimpling his cheeks. You touched his mouth to make the point that he had a tongue, too. He began inching his own tongue through his lips. It then became obvious that he had learned something. You had been his teacher. Every time he caught sight of you, his tongue popped in and out . . .

And by this ready discipleship I was most dreadfully alarmed. I saw, soon enough, the reason for my uneasiness: in this small morning incident, the whole horror of being a teacher was exposed. The lesson was so dubious: the pupil so innocent. I'd taught Tom something perfectly useless. And might he not take it to be one of life's fundamental activities?

'*Number in class:* 1. *Age range:* 0–2 months.

'*Aim of lesson:* To teach a basic technique of disgracefully rude behaviour—'

114

10

Barnacre, when I arrived for my first day's teaching, turned out
to be worse than I'd feared, and better. It was worse in a scarcely
credible fashion in respect of the way it was organised. I entered
the staffroom at 9.15, being booked for an arithmetic lesson at
10 o'clock. 'Sit there,' I was advised, 'until you see some activity.'
I thought this would be related to the timetable. Instead, it
seemed to be tied to spontaneous spasms of resolve, rather rare
ones, among the staff. By 9.30 the room was full of people taking
their ease, chattering. There were rumours of an assembly
occurring somewhere in the building—far out along one of those
bungaloid arms, perhaps. Occasionally a man would rise and
ask: 'Are they in?' He would then sit down again. It was
altogether as if a rather ragged press conference in London were
waiting for news over the wire from China. 10 o'clock came and
went. There was still no sign that, so far as the bulk of staff was
concerned, the school day would consist of anything but conversation. And the solving of crossword puzzles. Little groups were
already at work over *Daily Telegraphs* and *News Chronicles*.

One of those spasms, without apparent cause, occurred at
10.15. I reached the classroom, marooned at the end of a
corridor, at 10.20. My lesson notes had made no allowance for
telescoping. It didn't go badly: but I talked much too fast and
—perhaps under the influence of the building—found myself
going out along ill-advised corridors of digression. I thought my
exposition too bare, and decided to enrich it. I was soon puzzling
myself, as well as them. They began to bubble. It was no worse
than that—but exactly like the early stage of water beginning to
boil. Another ten minutes and they'd have been pouring over
the top of the pot.

'NB,' I reported at the foot of my notes. 'There must be something wrong with my gestures. In this lesson, not for the first time, I saw a boy imitate the movements of my hand.'

Barnacre was better than I'd feared in respect of the friendliness of some members of the staff. There was the art master, who in appearance was a caricature of one, having a simply enormous beard, very much rounded, more topiary than beard. He was so interested in my morning that I told him about my problem with gestures. 'Well,' he said. 'You've got active hands, I notice. You probably let them fly a bit, when talking to the kids. They notice everything, of course. Well, is anyone ever so much exposed to inspection by the bored and idle as a teacher? I don't mean you were boring.'

'I was worse than that.'

'Well, they love watching you, taking you to pieces—putting you together again, slightly crooked. Don't worry. I mean, unless you were . . . scratching your private parts, or anything like that.'

'Oh no,' I said with a vehemence of which I was at once ashamed. I had no wish to set myself up as a fanatical opponent of the scratching of private parts.

'Well, don't let it make you self-conscious.'

On the edge of a crossword puzzle group I found myself daring to suggest a solution. I was immediately made one of the group. I'd started the day disdaining teachers who gave their breaks to puzzles. I ended it with a distinct sense of the honour of being one of the co-operative committed to cracking the puzzle in the *Chronicle*. It seemed to be indicated that my services would be welcome the next day.

In the afternoon, at the suggestion of their regular English master, I turned Class 7 into balladmakers. I provided the first verse.

> A boy went into a garden once,
> Alas! 'twas not his own!
> He threw a stone into a tree.
> An apple fell with the stone.

'Guard,' said my notes, 'against stultification of their efforts by the difficulty of finding rhymes. If necessary, give discreet assistance.' This was not the word for the assistance I found myself giving. The muse of one small troubadour proposed that he write :

> And as the boy looked up at it
> The apple fell on his head,
> And then they found that this poor boy
> Was very very dead . . .

This was a model of rhythm and good sense compared with many of the verses provided. 'I don't think,' said my comment, 'that in normal circumstances—i.e. given one's own class—it would be advisable to start verse-making with so relatively advanced a form as the ballad. For every reasonable effort there was one that was merely silly.'

It could have been said, of course, of poetry at all levels throughout the ages.

'Discipline not wonderful,' I noted. 'I didn't really get on top of their bubbliness.' Then I added : 'It really was like teaching lemonade.' But Kate, reading anxiously over my shoulder, a curiously hooting naked son tucked under her arm, persuaded me to scratch it out. 'It's really not very good,' she said. 'If you'll accept my discreet assistance.'

Extraordinary that staffroom, in the morning. It wasn't always cheerfully uninterested in the timetable. Sometimes its lack of interest was glum. I was reminded of our local railway station.

The ticket office, and a road, were carried on a bridge above the platforms, and in the supporting brickwork of this bridge there were dark niches, of densely blue engineering brick. Many of my fellow-travellers stood inside these niches, stuffed away there, silent, some plainly morose : victims, I thought, of a gloomy impulse to hide, to remain free to brood, rather dismally. Perhaps I was wrong about this : perhaps they skulked in those niches in order to enjoy without interruption an extraordinary delight in life that needed to be savoured alone. But there was this dark silence, and every niche stuffed with its solitary brooder : and one morning I saw how like the Barnacre staffroom it was, and the one at Eastbourne Road. And how like the way most school days began, certainly at Barnacre, with irritable self-isolating persons assembling in a room that ought, perhaps, to have offered them niches to stand in: signalling, possibly with the help of some such dark brickwork, their wish to be left severely alone.

And how into that mood of gloom the children would burst, notably ungloomy, most of them: those that *were* gloomy, usually dramatically and noisily so. The bright roar and clatter of children arriving, and the adult gloom intensified: as if a great mass headache had run into a great mass intention of making headaches worse. So, very often the first half hour or so of the day, once Barnacre had got itself to its feet, was taken up with the consequences of this clash between adult sullenness, and juvenile brightness and noise. Boys in grave trouble for failing to talk in modest whispers: boys positively punished for asking questions, offering jokes, seeking justice (or, of course, injustice), failing to move about on tiptoe: being chatteringly brimful of last night and this morning: totally failing in solicitude towards their adult companions . . .

11

I had worked for hours on this chart of the battle for Quebec. It stretched across two yards of drawing paper, and was an amazing matter of blocks of colour, of flying, curving arrows, retreating and advancing. The blue loops of the St Lawrence river positively excited me. I only hoped that I could remember what it was all about. As I worked into it my slow understanding of the movement of armies, each item of understanding tended to vanish, erased by the next. I rehearsed my use of it with Kate as audience: though she'd been in tears that evening, as so often now, crying because Tom had been unhappy, had tried (and failed) to combine suction with lamentation. And she'd cried also because he was a tyrant: and the two of us together hardly seemed to slave fast enough for him. 'Are you with me?' I asked, hoping this old battle might take her mind off new ones. 'I can't think how men could behave like that to one another,' Kate said. 'Oh please—you're not to adopt a philosophical view . . . *Please*. The children aren't going to look at it like that.' 'Perhaps they should,' said Kate, hotly. She was disastrously inclined to favour the French. I thought Marie might have been talking to her. 'Please think patriotically,' I begged her. Kate said sadly: 'I never expected to hear you say anything like that.' Political guilt was added to my nervousness. Was she right? Should I be offering the lesson as an example of man's inhumanity to man? Should I at least be rooting for the French, to correct the chauvinistic slant of our history teaching?

I entered the classroom, next morning, in an unpromising state. Not only was I baffled by my own studies: I was also unconfident of the very validity of the lesson. But these questions soon came to seem very academic indeed. There was an air, in the room, of not precisely knowing where Canada was, and what these people were doing, quarrelling about Quebec. But even that was a secondary element in the situation. The immediate matter was one simply of justifying my presence in the room. 'Where's Mr Higgs, then?' 'Look, I'm taking this lesson. Let's get on with it.' 'Mr Higgs said he was going to tell us about pirates.' 'Pirates? What do you mean, pirates?' 'We're talking about pirates with Mr Higgs.' 'The Spanish Main.' 'Skull and crossbones.' 'Look here, you're doing colonial history this term.' 'What's he talking about?'

I seemed to persuade them, after a while, that Canada, if not a legitimate subject for study, was to be the theme of this lesson, beyond all prospect of appeal. They settled themselves into a disgruntled and unhopeful readiness. I began what I thought of as: The Story So Far. In my preparation I'd assumed this would be the simplest reminder of work they'd done already with Mr Higgs. I was now extremely doubtful that they'd done, with Mr Higgs, any work at all. He had been gossiping with them about pirates . . .

Was that possible? He'd given no impression of being a liar. Was this a ploy directed against the hapless student?

My uncertainty total, I tried not to see their blank faces— not to hear their cries of puzzlement.

The French? The St Lawrence? Orders from London? 1757? What was this infatuated intruder talking about?

I'd save the situation—of course the situation could be saved —with my visual aid. I would pin it to the blackboard and their attention would be riveted. The art work would amaze them, the excitements of battle would dismiss their doubts . . .

I unrolled the chart, opened my box of drawing pins, and pressed the first pin into the top lefthand corner of the board.

The board was made of something like iron. The pin collapsed. There was laughter. I tried another. It collapsed. I tried one more. There was a great deal of laughter.

No ordinary drawing pin, urged by a mere thumb, would ever penetrate that surface.

Why had there never been a major lecture at Isleden on the fallibility of drawing pins and the treachery of blackboards?

The chart rolled itself up in my agitated hand. It turned into a telescope and somersaulted out of my grasp. I bent down and picked it up. 'Stop that noise!' I rushed across to a cupboard door and pinned down one side of the chart—then unrolled it. It was several feet too long. To pin the other side to, there was nothing but air.

It ended with awful angers on my part which, even as they vented themselves, struck me as totally beside the point. That such a lofty enterprise as my lesson had been meant to be, supported by so superb an aid as my battle-chart, should fall to the ground through a foolish matter of drawing pins . . . how funny that was, and surely I should be adding my laughter to the wild amusement of the class. But I was possessed by horror and rage, and unable to prevent myself from bringing these to bear on, really, the silliest of all the grievances I'd amassed.

They sat, quivering, whispering, their hands on their heads ('Do you know, they still make kids sit with hands on heads,' I'd told Ben recently), while I prowled up and down hissing: 'Pirates! Pirates indeed! I shall check with Mr Higgs about pirates! What do you mean by saying the lesson was to be about pirates!'

And so on.

I think of that second teaching practice as a queer, dark experience. I lost the middle of it, being in bed with the 'flu. It was a thin, sour February: I hated my winter clothes—felt about my hat as if it were a prison I'd put my head into. I didn't like the mildly false position of being a student, practising. There were times when I didn't like the teacher's life at all.

There were suddenly absentees on the staff—I was needed as a stopgap. Everybody became ominously affable, and I knew I was in trouble. 'Class 2—make up your own timetable. Make yourself at home with them. All right, old man?' I guessed it wasn't all right, but smiled.

The difficulties I had, for the next few days, sprang from that invitation to invent my own timetable, and the absence of all guidance. Well, you could get lost at the end of a corridor, and that's where I was. And there was this outbreak of 'flu, and it had scattered the crossword schools, the staffroom becoming largely empty and wholly distraught. I went with increasing reluctance down the corridor to Class 2, and made up my time-table.

I simply didn't seem to have the material for it. It was horrific, to be at the shop counter, as it were, and to reach back to the shelves behind, and find them empty. My work at the prep school had always been very formally plotted out, shaped by the precise needs of the Common Entrance exam, buttressed by Smith's *Sixpenny Arithmetic*, Brown's *Shilling English Course*. At Isleden I'd worked within the careful, parched confines of lesson notes. And now, with Class 2 all day for everything, I had nothing to give. Geography, nothing. History, nothing. Arithmetic, nothing. English, not very much.

'What am I doing,' I asked my unresponsive diary, 'masquerading as a teacher? I ought to sack myself.'

The truth is that I was like someone who'd been introduced to a trick cupboard. I'd been given a key to open it, and there was this shallow interior, with meagre contents. I didn't know that the apparent back of the cupboard was another door, and if I opened *that*, everything would be there. Well, everything I possessed, by way of knowledge, ideas, inventiveness. But I was fooled by this shallow, trick cupboard, and thought I had nothing to give.

A sterile game based on the dictionary, for English. If I wanted to show them something about words, the fact that words were my own first passion should have helped. I had only to be myself, to begin working with them, with words. Well, I could have made something, something at once rueful and useful, out of my awareness of my own appetite, so often absurd, for verbal thunder, great verbal roarings. The material was there, in the hidden part of the cupboard. The night before, for example, when Tom, from being remote from us, sunk in milky stupor, had suddenly been appallingly awake, uttering deep desperate howls. We'd examined this steaming bundle in an attempt to discover some cause for such stridency. I suddenly recognised, as an old agriculturalist, the smell of his face—it was like the interior of a mill. *'Facially farinaceous!'* I cried. 'Oh for goodness sake say something helpful,' said Kate.

My supervising tutor this time was a mathematician, Straker. He said : 'Well, yes, you're all right, it's really all right. But you could relax a little you know. You could risk a little humour, a little lightness. You were very solemn . . . And do stop juggling with pieces of chalk !'

Lacking in humour! But I had a gross appetite for jokes—my whole mind had always been helplessly ticklish ! How could I have declined into a situation where I was being exhorted to display lightheartedness? As to juggling with chalk—did I really do that? An effort of recall informed me that I did. Walking about the room, I tossed sticks of chalk from hand to hand. Why? Nerves, yes, but—Then I remembered my old Latin master at school. He always juggled with chalk. It was the one highlight of lessons sorely in need of highlights—our fascinated observation of those pieces of chalk as they flew from hand to hand. Would he drop one? Or, since he always did that in the end, *when* would he drop one?

I realised that, in the attempt to convince myself that I was a teacher, I was parodying the men who taught me. I was becoming a sort of imitative composite of old Frosty, Goof, Eros, Poker, Knobby—the whole menagerie of my former instructors. Those walking nicknames . . .

12

So far from being at ease! So far from being myself! It made me think of John Logan, an Irishman, one of those former instructors. We called him, of course, Loganberry.

He'd known how to make school life glow . . . first, by way of a kind of ridiculous employment of flattery. He'd give boys titles. You'd be creeping along a corridor, feeling small and dull, and he would appear, crying: 'And how is my Lord Archbishop today?' The entire scene would brighten. First year boys who thought themselves invisible were startled to have viscountcies or marquisates conferred upon them, or exotic ambassadorships. For a long time, and without reference to the actual owner of the title, I was the Duke of St Albans, on the slim grounds that John Logan had once caught sight of me in that town with Roger Bunce, on a Wednesday afternoon when we should have been playing rugger. 'Will Your Grace be dignifying the game today?' he'd inquire, terms later. By the time I'd established my lack of appetite for games, he'd become one of our sporting overlords: and, having carefully written me out of B game, as well as all games known by other letters, he'd say: 'We shan't be requesting Your Grace's presence this afternoon. You'll be in the North Tower, I imagine, reading Milton.'

It was always Milton. One year I'd gone in for the school's Poetry Essay Prize: subject, Milton's sonnets. Logan, catching me in a corridor, said: 'I think Your Grace will find himself understanding Milton better at forty than at fourteen.' Thereafter the idea persisted that I was spending most of my time puzzling over the sonnets. I became a non-athletic senior peer of the realm with a poetic problem. Twenty years later I met him in the street and he said: 'Have you got to the bottom of them yet, Princess?'—a change of title that sprang from his having

E   123

decided, one day in 1934, that I resembled a beautiful Greek recently arrived in England. 'You look just like Marina, Your Grace.' Since I was on my way back from the playing fields, it was, I can only say, a muddy and, as to the knees, mildly bloody Marina, wearing someone else's rugger shirt, that he had in mind.

Somehow, with him, it wasn't whimsy. It was an aspect of his enchanting good humour, and of his refusal to take life altogether seriously. There was also a touch of the wistful fallen gentleman about him. His family, he would tell us in thrilling lessons that had only the slightest relation to mathematics—to which they were supposed to be devoted—the Logans had once been rich, able to devote themselves entirely to the arts and to stylish varieties of idleness. There had been a decline, itself very elegant. He'd been appointed to the staff, I believe, largely because he was a lawn tennis international—though we didn't play lawn tennis. That seemed to be why, in the lower school, he took us for mathematics—there being, I suppose, an obvious connection with tennis: love–15, 15–30 and so on. He was, in fact, mathematically quite inept. He should have taken us for . . . oh, General Fantasy, Literature at Random, Extremely General Knowledge. He bubbled with odd information—eccentric queries that led, at times, to marvellous books in neglected corners of the school library. Well, as to books, show the mildest interest and you'd find novels or volumes of verse being mysteriously transferred into your custody in corridors, as if they'd been betting slips. 'Keep it quiet,' he'd say, sometimes. The school's general outlook tended to be that its task of turning us into gentlemen was grossly imperilled by the writings of D. H. Lawrence, Aldous Huxley, George Orwell. Safest to frown on all new writing. Thus John Logan's finger on his lips. Once, with me, it was *Tess of the D'Urbervilles* that was the cause of his caution: and it was forty years too late to keep quiet about that.

But then he knew the teacherly value of conspiracy as well as that of flattery. Even a formal lesson with him, though the phrase isn't suitable, was a conspiracy. You got into a huddle and he told you about the great days of the Logans, in Ireland. Or he embarked on the extraordinary operation that was meant to give these occasions at least a faintly mathematical air.

124

Batches of Five: sequences of mental arithmetic questions. They'd have, to begin with, some plausible numerical ingredient. 'Who were the Nine Muses?' Thereafter they drifted, charmingly, into little-frequented creeks and inlets of General Knowledge. Or General Ignorance, really. They also turned accidents into opportunities. So after Mrs Porter, the handsome school secretary, had left the room with the day's list of absentees, came Question Four in the current batch. 'What is the colour of Mrs Porter's eyes?' She had the lustful adoration of us all, but none was certain of the answer. It was a sort of learning, I think. You had discovered that you could be in love and still not have noted the colour of the beloved's eyes.

He took me once to see *The Beggar's Opera*. First we lunched at his club. I had an uneasy idea of what such a place might be, based on a rather mixed sort of reading: Sapper and Galsworthy and P. G. Wodehouse, for example. The meal took place, as it seemed to me (though it was a day of nervous blurring of vision), in the library. I was startled, not having understood from the literature that one ate in libraries. I was rash enough to order a pork chop, which came with extremely brittle crackling: when I cut it, a fragment flew across the room, to land on some remote part of the splendid carpet. A flunkey came out of the shadows with a napkin and bore my piece of crackling away and I never saw it again. At fifteen I was socially ruined. On the day my larger life had begun, it was over . . .

In the theatre I was saved by Logan's eleventh-hour cry from sitting on his bowler hat, which was of the wickeder kind, with a curling brim, and had belonged to his father, who I always thought of, with no documentary justification, as the Logan of Logan.

If I was to be a teacher, I wanted to be a cross between John Logan and Mr Salt: but here I was, a humourless juggler with chalk. I was, in fact, the victim of the light-heartedness of others. There was a boy in Class 2 who was, I had to conclude, an advanced delinquent—yet his offence was barely definable. The nearest I could come to it was to say that he turned sitting down into a comedy. He did nothing outrageous—didn't slip clownishly off the seat onto the floor, or anything like that—but his way of sitting down was distinctly funny, and it caused laughter.

Dealing with this was beyond me. I could only reflect how impossible it was to shout: 'Don't sit down *comically*!'

I mentioned it in the staffroom, meaning it as a joke at my expense: but they said, earnestly: 'You have to squash him!' Well, if you had to, then you had to: but I thought of all the boys I'd left unsquashed. If to be a teacher you must be a squasher, then I was ruled out, at once. I knew the process, of course. At Barnacre it was engaged in, almost all the time, by a teacher called Hatt.

There'd be some group of boys halted, frozen, and Hatt would be saying: 'Well, now, this won't do—will it, lads? Will it, Dobbs?' Dobbs would shrug his shoulders. 'Will it, Fry?' Fry would offer a cross between a grin and a yawn. 'Will it, Gates?' From Gates, an uneasy whimper. Hatt was capable of putting his rhetorical question to thirty or forty boys in succession, squashingly, until the whole group was squirming with the agony of it. Well, it *was* agony to be so slowly, meticulously exposed to the unanswerable. 'We don't want to get a bad name, do we?' If they were lucky, he'd not solicit individual responses to that one. 'We're fed up with being told not to dash about, aren't we? Well, look here, lads. You can take it from me that, if there's any more of it, if I see a single boy going along a corridor faster than walking pace, then I'll—What will I do, laddie?' This question flashed at a boy whose eye, for a split second, had wandered. Laddie too appalled to provide an answer. 'Right. Stay and see me afterwards, laddie. I'll do what, Dobbs?' And so on through all those names until some boy nerved himself to satisfy the man. 'You'll come down on us like a ton of bricks, sir.' 'Right, Kirk. What did Kirk say, Chester?'

Waiting for Hatt, whose class I was to take, I'd find my head beginning to spin. There seemed no reason why this appalling chain of false questions shouldn't go on for ever. Ten minutes after the original offence, they'd still be there, hangdog, deeply bored, cautiously fidgety.

I found on waking some days that I'd been dreaming about Hatt. Something awfully interesting was happening and then he'd appeared, he'd brought the whole world to a halt, from pole to pole we were giving him our nervous, glazed attention. It occurred to me that Hatt was very much like the war—that was perhaps why his performances had so haunting an effect on me.

126

For six years we'd been held up by those murderous traffic-lights, by something that on the hugest scale was as negative and nagging as Hatt himself.

The awful thing was that the boys respected him. They were impressed by his total lack of humour and imagination. In some sense he was what they thought a teacher should be : unremittingly dissatisfied, never reluctant to bring everything to a long, shrewish halt.

But then there was Brimley, in charge of Class 4, A stream third year, who was no squasher at all. He was simply charming —a man with a dilettante air. I sat with him once when he took an unprepared lesson with Class 2, who were capable of being turned into jesters by my mere appearance. He chose to talk to them about seventeenth century architecture. If you'd drawn up a list of subjects least likely to interest Class 2, this was one of which the unsuitability would not begin to be expressed by putting it at the bottom. Just possibly the most cunningly vivid use of language might have helped. Brimley's language was utterly wrong for his audience : full of words, phrases, terms quite beyond them. Having made a far too complex remark he would set out to make it more complex, introducing reservations, qualifications, doubts (by which they'd not been bothered) propounded and answered.

And they listened. They listened without protest. Some were clearly far away, but quietly, contentedly, carefully so. His voice, I noticed, came slowly, in a totally relaxed fashion. He might, in some club, late in the evening, after an excellent dinner and much good wine and port, have been turning over a few ideas in a little circle of seventeenth century experts. He even yawned at one point.

How, from all this, to piece together some notion of the quality of a teacher?

I was beginning to see clearly, at Barnacre, that in teaching, so much could be done, or so little! It was tremendously easy to coast along, to lie back. Laziness could become an occupation : it could also wear a busy, bustling mask. There was Miller, a senior master, always dashing down corridors, entering classrooms to communicate urgent banalities to his colleagues, and rarely reaching his own room. An immense noise was often Miller's class paying the price of their master's industrious idleness. He made me think of a phrase of Mr Jepp's, one that haunted me for years, surviving long after his stale and awestruck summaries of Plato and Locke had faded. 'Hard teaching.' Mr Jepp talked of hard teaching as a boxer might talk of a correctly delivered uppercut. Boxing was having the intention of knocking out your opponent—it wasn't anything else. In the same way, teaching revolved uniquely round an intention of teaching. While expounding this idea, which was passionately his own, and which he dwelt on in daily paroxysms, Mr Jepp would illustrate the spirit of it by setting up a contest between his left hand, open-palmed, representing the human tendency to inertia, and his right hand, balled, standing for: *hard teaching*. There were times when you feared inertia might come out of it with a broken wrist, at least.

13

Well, you presumably could be a teacher by being fearfully unattractive, like Hatt—or fearfully attractive, like Brimley . . .

Barnacre's headmaster returned from sick leave: a fact his deputy chose to announce at assembly with the words: 'Mr Mobbs is back.' 'Hooray!' came loud cries from all over the hall. Since it was clear that there was no great affection for Mr Mobbs, these cries amounted to a declaration of the deputy's quite tremendous unpopularity. 'Come out,' he raged, 'the boys who shouted hooray.' Even as he spoke, his face, dark with anger, paled with perplexity. How could he condemn boys for apparently being quite transported with pleasure at their headmaster's recovery and return? Large amounts of anger, still not used up, gave an odd tone to his voice as he roared: 'All right! You may have meant well. But . . . just don't *shout*!' Then he seemed to realise that he was shouting. 'Just *don't* shout!' he repeated in a tiny voice.

One small triumph, out of the blue, quite unrelated to over-night preparation. To a first year class I announced a poetry lesson. Their dismay was so dramatic that I was shaken out of all my grooves. 'But why does that make you unhappy?' I cried. 'Poetry!' said a boy, as if the term itself contained his entire argument. But what was wrong with poetry? They struggled for words to express their distaste. 'Too *long*,' said one. They cried out, then, together, and all turned to the boy, smiling. He had the prize for the year's most superbly chosen epithet. I found, and read to them, a poem by Eleanor Farjeon, on cats—a spit and hiss of a poem, that just has time to arch its back. They were stunned. They asked for it again : once, to have the ridiculous illusion of pleasure dispelled : and when that didn't work, a second time, for pure, astonished enjoyment. Intoxicated, I read them a dozen of the tiniest poems I could find. At the end of the lesson I was positively applauded.

I left the room feeling a cross between Mr Jepp, Mr Salt and John Gielgud.

At once I went to a lesson with Class 3. 'Talk to them', a hurried teacher had suggested, ' about debating.' They were, he alleged, very eager to know the techniques of formal discussion. They could hardly wait. He himself found it only just possible to hand over to me this unusually welcome piece of teaching . . . Their air, when I met them, was not of that sort of eagerness. But I began, still feeling famous and successful, with talk of pros and cons. To be exact, I began with talk of pros : and was at once engulfed in inexplicable laughter, noises of an unfamiliar kind, uncontrollable jubilation. Only slowly did it dawn on me, as I tried to slash my way out of the jungle of misconduct that I'd so mysteriously created, that, in Seven Elms, the term 'pros' did not commonly refer to arguments supporting some motion or resolution.

I left the room feeling quite tragically myself.

What I hated most at Barnacre, if I was right about it, was a kind of shared cynicism between some teachers and the children. 'The whole thing's a farce,' was the implication. 'You know it, and we know it. Which of us really cares about the use of the comma, or equations, or the poetry of William Words-worth? We're not going to pretend we want to teach these things, and you'll not pretend that you want to learn about them. You're a coarse lot of kids, and we're a coarse lot of teachers. Let's keep it like that.' Of course, it was never made explicit, in that fashion : but this was the nature of the contract between the two sides. It went back, it seemed to me, an awfully long way into the history of the schools : further back, into social history. It was the acceptance of a gulf, that made it certain that a gulf would continue to exist.

But must the gulf exist? Must there be, over here, people—teachers and children—who, cheerfully or otherwise, had accepted sharp limits to their way of thinking, their interests—their expectations of themselves? And, over there, people of the opposite inclination and habit? Yes, *habit*. Both camps surely did what they did as much from habit as anything else. What was needed was defiance of habit.

Who could tell what would happen if the teachers refused to accept this idea of their own, and the children's coarseness?

A good voice, said Straker on his last visit : a pleasant manner : but I was killing myself. Well, he'd come early, and hadn't expected to hear me reading *The Invisible Man* to Class 5—but really, it was the sort of reading that could lead to heart failure. No one could put out that amount of virtuoso energy very often in a school week. I'd been daring them to get up and leave the theatre! And then in this little drama lesson that followed—well, now I'd got them at work in groups, in corners, preparing scenes— 'Leave them alone for a while. They're all right.' He drove me into an empty seat. 'Quieten down. There's no possibility that you'll be failed, you know.'

Well, yes, I had this preposterous dread of failure. But beyond it, I think, lay the angry puzzlement of knowing that, whatever Straker said—whatever anyone said—I was miles from discovering how to teach. I was light years away from being John Logan. I hadn't a clue how to become Mr Salt.

Barnacre was an unsatisfactory place, architecturally self-defeating, with a limping staff, poorly led. Yet I'd begun to grow into the staffroom, had begun to have some knowledge of some boys. Now it was all over again : cut short : and it was back to Isleden, secondhand Plato, the combined course.

Nature study, among other things. There'd been that occasion

130

when soft Mr Dash, Biology and R.I., had induced us to listen to the sound of a worm walking across a sheet of paper. The unexpected thunder of its progress had caused Bing to imagine music, alas, never written, by a collaboration of composers that never occurred: *Grand March of the Worms*, by Berlioz, arr. Sousa . . .

But damn it, what I really wanted to do was to get on with discovering how to teach.

Meanwhile, there was Tom. Had to be worthy of being his father: which the man under Class 2's thumb hardly was. A queer thing, intimacy with that absolute babyhood. To be so concerned with someone so far back along the road of experience. Always, to some extent, he seemed a fictitious character. Kate and I had made him up.

He celebrated the end of my second teaching practice by leaning back on Kate's lap, bloated with milk: for all the world like some old ham actor. His face infinitely secular, he allowed himself to be the mouthpiece of hoots, splutters, squeaks, smackings of the lips, deep clearings of the throat. He twitched with enormous gout. Then Kate undressed him, and, at last putting all thought of Barnacre behind me, I joined her in staring at the belly of this decadent thespian of our creation— a preposterous thing, his belly, like nothing so much as an overfull wineskin . . .

PART THREE

1

'And then,' Broom told us, 'she got dressed and cooked me eggs and bacon.' He turned and stared at the man standing at his other elbow. It was Mr Jepp. 'I wonder,' murmured Bing, from behind, 'into what code that will be translated, in your testimonial.'

My pleasant relations with Broom amounted to friendship across a divide that had opened up at school—between science and the arts. My ignorance of simple science amazed him: at times, in fact, he made rather too much of his disbelief that I could know so little. 'My God,' he'd exclaim, much too loud: 'this is terrible proof of what I've been told, but never believed till now: that the *intelligentsia* simply don't live in the same century as the rest of us.' 'Oh come, Broom,' I'd say, as half the college turned its head to listen. 'Amazing,' Broom would cry. 'Such *affectation* of not knowing what a moving coil does in a loudspeaker.' 'Oh, don't shout,' I'd plead. 'And it's not an affectation, you know.'

We had become, I think, a parody of the divide between science and the arts. Because he'd be dramatic, too, about my acquaintance with books and music. 'My goodness,' he'd roar, again in a manner that drew crowds. 'How is it possible that this . . . physically quite slight fellow, without the assistance of modern aids—of which he knows nothing—how is it possible that he has read, and remembered, so much!' 'I only said,' I would mumble, 'that if you wanted an example of the very long novel that can seem, because of the pleasure of reading it, very short— a *silly* remark, anyway—you've only got to pick up *Bleak House*.' 'He says, you notice,' Broom would roar, 'that you've only got to pick it up! Such nonchalance!'

Under the absurdity of such exchanges, there was an honest

astonishment on my side, as to his grasp of science : and a similar amazement on his part, as to my having read so many books and being capable of recognising so much music. Though, as to music, I always felt at a disadvantage vis-à-vis Broom. His current lady was an infants' school teacher. Broom had no reticence : he was perfectly frank about their habit of making love to music. 'Have you,' he would cry, 'tried it to the slow movement of Dvorak's cello concerto?' It was a new dimension of musical criticism. There was a long sequence of experiments related to the symphonies of Brahms. 'Old Johannes knew a thing or two,' Broom would say, as if the process of composing those symphonies had resembled the process of enjoying them embarked upon by Broom and his friend. 'When I think,' said Broom, 'that she goes more or less straight from one of our sessions and teaches her little ones the alphabet . . . My goodness!' There was always, when he said such a thing, an impression of applause, or at any rate a kind of strangled clapping, from Dvorak, Brahms and others among Broom's immortal accomplices.

It was the edge of spring again. There was a blue day when the sky was like a china bowl, with trees painted black on the rim : it ended with a coppery foliage of light in the taller trees round the cricket field we faced from the flat. Our son had become a spring creature—in some almost literal sense : disposing of as much energy as a whole team of athletes, he leapt like a high jumper if his feet merely touched a lap.

At Isleden, the run to the tape. There'd be interviews with the representatives of local authorities. The quest for employment would be woven into a pattern of final school practice and general end-of-course activities.

And the unreality of it grew worse.

It was unreality and a debilitating cynicism, together. It arose partly, I think, because some of the lecturers, aware that they were dealing largely with ex-servicemen, were terrified of being found naïve. They tried, therefore, to look and sound free of illusion. They made a parade of educational worldliness. The realism of doing so was only apparent. It did not connect with what, in a great many students, was a very important reality : their wish simply to do something rather splendid, as teachers.

That eternal teacher-training seesaw of ideal and reality . . .

And this cynicism (using in careful quotation marks such words as 'flannel' and 'bullshit') bred the dominant characters of the course: the swashbucklers and the windowdressers.

On the other side there was, particularly, Mr Salt: who seemed to breathe so freely and happily in an atmosphere in which many were choking. If he was aware of the way students were being torn between false fact and false vision, he showed no sign of it. He went on smiling his invaluable smile. And it was under his quiet chairmanship, in Op Lit, that a student equally quiet, the very reverse of a windowdresser, talked to us for two periods about the Brontes. His childhood home had been near Haworth, the family had interested him since he was a school-boy: he talked sturdily out of this long, straight interest, taking *our* interest for granted. It made me feel we had only ourselves to blame if we surrendered to the prevailing pretence of thick skin, cold blood. After all, the cynics, the windowdressers, were wrong: the steady enthusiasts were right. This quiet straight Yorkshireman would be ten times the teacher that most of his noisy subtle rivals would be.

The atmosphere had gone wrong, too, for some, because of immemorial impossibilities in the very character of teacher-training. Mr Jepp, for example, said that too many would-be teachers thought first of themselves, rather than of the children. It was a useful thing to have said: and yet, unqualified, a little like asserting that the learner at ski-ing thought of his feet, and not of the general skill of ski-ing. It might have been better if Mr Jepp had said that inevitably one had to think of oneself—those teacherly legs and arms so difficult to control: but that one should work through that stage as fast as possible, bearing in mind that the aim was to reverse the order of importance: children first, yourself second. There was nothing clear-cut about it, at all: but a sense of reality should tell you that the desirable was to be achieved only by an approach through layers of the less desirable.

Of course it was right for Mr Jepp to say what he said. But it was only *half*-right. The trouble with teacher training was that it shrank, rather, from admitting that as a teacher you had to fall on your nose again and again before you could safely walk a couple of yards. The banana-skins were left out, the custard pies, all the booby-traps and general ignominies.

2

Ben was attending classes in Eng Lit, and had found *them* a booby-trap. He didn't think he'd persist with them. To begin with, he didn't care for the lecturer. She'd been talking about Blake, whom Ben had never before looked at closely : but had not made up her mind how to approach Blake's visions, treating them alternately as awe-inspiring facts ('He saw into another dimension') and as jokes. 'I don't much care for these people who swing on the boughs of literature,' said Ben. But he was happily writing an essay on Blake. The problem was reading him, or any other poet. 'In my job I'm so used now to gutting documents and books.' I suggested a title for the essay : 'On First Gutting Blake'.

In the shadow of the production of *Macbeth*, all sorts of excuses were being found for acting. Bing was deeply hooked. His lucidity, his coolness, his witty detachment gave way altogether under the excitements of the drama. Told that he'd cut lines of importance in an Op Maths production of some thin one-acter, Bing rushed to the lavatory and shut himself in and wept. Trotsky could not help him. All the mathematicians in the world were suddenly impotent. In a ridiculous matter of his representing some entirely invented character in some mild simulation of real life, Bing had skipped a few of the lines apportioned to him, and the result was total and devastating misery. He was red-eyed still when I met him in a corridor. 'How our vanities are caught up in this business of acting,' he muttered. 'Bing,' I said, momentarily the stronger, 'it's not vanity. It's something awfully difficult to control—our feelings in respect of the attempt to get some emotional equation right.'

Bing made a face and we trudged together down the corridor, not unhappily silent.

It was absolutely right, of course, that we should have been shown that thinking about education didn't begin five minutes ago. But it would have been interesting to know how often, off the platform—say, in the company of Mrs Jepp—our famous stormy-eyed lecturer on the aims and philosophy of education spoke of Plato.

If only, I've thought often since, we'd been given some amused, even comic introduction to the character of human ideas, to the circularity of their arrival on the scene—in education, particularly, the tendency of ideas thousands of years old to emerge with a very plausible appearance of new-mintedness. It could have been fun—a game of ideas. Intellectual gym . . . philosophical basketball . . .

Mr Potton, P.E. and Health, kept theory at a scalpel's length. To Mr Potton, the worst aspects of mortality were the substance of lectures. He took us, but rather absent-mindedly, to London's largest medical museum. Two hundred students entered and came out again, two hundred hypochondriacs. Bing said it was a glimpse of a field of which, to his knowledge, Marxism provided no account. Broom said he was not issuing an immediate statement, but his friends could take it that his continued participation in the affairs of the world was under gloomy consideration.

My own nerve was weakened for a while : even though this was a time when Kate and I were daily delighted by demonstrations of constructive mortality : the way Tom was translating milk into vigorous substance.

Kate was inclined to blame Plato and his philosophical colleagues for what she took to be a refusal of sensuous wholeheartedness on my part. There were times, she held, when I was quite as bad as Ben in the matter of keeping romance at bay. In my case, I think now, it was an awful defensive mischief, a dread (oh, so related to those wars of realism and idealism) of being absolutely affirmative, wholly enthusiastic. I'd noticed that when Kate said a thing was exciting or beautiful, my feeling of agreement instantly tucked itself away, embarrassed. I began to look round for defects. I was scared of her liking things so fully and instantly and gladly. I thought, off and on, that she lacked all perception of flaws. It pleased me when we found ourselves agreeing in disliking something.

Kate had cried, on one of these spring evenings, when we were wheeling Tom round the cricket field (he being engaged in his current love affair with the sky, cooing at it): 'If you find some part of me to approve of, do tell me, won't you! My hair is wiry and dull'—I'd said it was like a cushion of couch-grass—'my forehead is too big'—I'd said it had nobility—'I have a moustache'—I'd feigned to be tickled by her kisses—'I'm too thin'—exaggerated praise of her slenderness—'and I have hockey legs' —I'd said that I liked a girl to be substantially based.

'Oh,' I said, as Romeo would certainly not have done: 'I daresay we'll find some nook or cranny to think well of.'

I do not understand why Kate did not commit what would have been forgivable murder. Instead she resorted to a quotation: 'Your wife is no broomstick, sir!'

The phrase had been addressed to me, the summer before our marriage, by a young Frenchman. We'd been on holiday to Italy: Kate's first visit abroad, my second. For us both the incredibility of things foreign was very strong. We could not really be in Paris, Milan, Florence, Venice. It was unlikely that this was in fact St Mark's. We lodged for a week in a villa we did not believe in, half-way between so-called Florence and alleged Fiesole. Because the Germans had taken all the coins, the tram conductors were unhappily busy men engaged in peeling one tattered note away from another, or applying patches of sellotape. Kate posed on the Lido for her photograph, slim in her bathing costume, leaning against a notice that forbade her to offend the public's susceptibility to shame. It all being Italian would have been enough to stun us: the beauty of buildings and paintings and sculpture made it too much. We returned, having in three weeks not quite spent our permitted £35, worn out with delight and disbelief.

And on the train between Paris and Dieppe, this young Breton, a scientist on his way to Essex for a year to teach and to polish his English. Extremely keen to exchange generalisations, he contended that the French were artists, who must always live artistically. That explained their gestures, of hand and body, he said, watching his own hands in flight, and laughing. The Englishman (I would of course forgive him) was a man of patience—he had, for example, his Fabianism. 'Ah, typical!' The Frenchman could not endure to sit around sleeping while things slowly developed : every now and then he must go out and riot. 'It is a kind of ballet.' The Frenchman liked to see life on the move.

He had, he said, this fiancée at home—a teacher, too : of mathematics, physics and, of course, cookery. 'A quiet soul, with great brevity of words . . . When I was a boy—I am always a boy, but in the sense of the phrase!—I had a little red fish. It was a quiet good soul—with great brevity of words. You see!' But he was rather hoping he might, during his year, have an English love. 'Something of dreams? *A Midsummer Night's Dream*?'

I hoped he was master of the plot of that play. It all sounded rather dangerous. I worried for the little red fish of a girl back in Brittany.

It was when Kate left the carriage that he leaned forward, with an air of someone who had a prize to confer. 'You are a lucky man!' he cried. 'Your wife is no broomstick, sir! She has charm and lightness. Yes, sir. She has great delicacy and explains things clearly and slowly to me.' He thought over what he'd said and decided that part of it was worth repetition : because, I guess, it was the statement of a discovery that ran counter to all expectation and prejudice in respect of English girls and their physique.

'Your wife is no broomstick, sir!'

'In other circumstances, Kate,' I said, thinking of one or two sexual nomads I'd encountered on the course, 'you wouldn't see me for lust.'

3

An inspector from the London County Council arrived in the college. One by one we sat opposite him. Ah, he said, in my case: I seemed . . . Yes, very good. Ah! No experience of teaching girls? No. Might find *that* useful. Make a point of it, eh?

'It says,' he remarked, midway, 'that you have an agreeable voice. Yes. Yes.' I wanted to tell him that my friend Broom said it was 'cut-glass'. 'General vicinity of Eton.' Oh Broom! It was general vicinity of Barton-on-the-hill, the bald end. Aitches provided by my English master at the grammar school, wanting me to play Richard II, and not keen on a monarch without aspirates. Vowels by courtesy of . . . oh, I supposed the BBC, John Logan, John Gielgud. Kate (elocution medal, 1932) faulted me on the pronunciation of 'revolt' and 'field'. A late invention, my voice.

The course was going to sleep. I was kept awake only by John Donne. 'The world created by his poetry is like no other poetic world—exacting, immediate, rousing. If we are sleepy when we enter it, we are soon jolted awake. Indeed, it is with a jolt that a poem by Donne begins.

> He is starke mad, who ever sayes
> That he hath been in love an houre,

or

> Who ever guesses, thinks or dreams he knowes
> Who is my mistris, wither by this curse.

This poetry does not woo our attention: it insists upon it, like a pistol shot.'

Ben suggested a title: 'On First Being Peppered by John Donne'.

142

Bing said: 'I feel we may have to put our heads together and re-examine our ideas about teaching . . . in the light of the possibility that this course has obscured rather than clarified them . . ."

Kate's hair hung in untended strings. The housework was never done. Tom was beginning to have a tiny, recognisable identity: and even we, his harassed slaves, could see it was an amiable one. He looked quite positively for grins to which to respond. His solemnity was reserved for people (and there were so many of them) who felt it was a matter of pride to prove they could make a baby smile.

But we found ourselves (in the split second between one day and the next) filled with the coarsest possible longing for fun. We didn't really know what we meant, hadn't time to define it: but what we probably had in mind, we thought, was something fairly scandalous. It might involve sustained public drunkenness: it would certainly revolve round almost continuous attendance at theatres and concert halls . . .

Kate's parents sat in for us and we went to hear a quartet. I thought: There you are—they're *musicians*! Not teachers! How strange! They're people publicly employed on ecstatic business!

I was (the phrase turned out to be) recommended for acceptance into the London County Council teaching service.

4

My third school practice was at Cannon Road Secondary Modern: a physically dim boys' school squeezed, with its sister school, into an inner suburban corner site. It gave an impression from the beginning of being, yes, actually cornered: hemmed in by a pandemonium of shops and small houses. The Head was a small, fussy, *hemmed-in* man who on our exploratory visit —

there were two of us—had treated us like . . . ten-year-olds, I thought. Baynes, my fellow-student, held that I was altogether too genial about that. 'It was seven-year-olds he had in mind,' said Baynes, who was going to teach in primary schools. 'When you speak that slow and loud, it's the smaller juniors you think you're talking to.'

At our first assembly the Head said: 'Today we welcome two students—Mr Umph and Mr Ah!' His notes eluded him. 'We're going to treat them with respect, aren't we, and not take advantage of them? We'll show them what Cannon Road can do, eh?'

The rustle and titter in the hall suggested a horrid 'No' to the first of these questions: an alarmingly ambiguous response to the second. The Head found his notes and went on confidently to make our task more difficult. 'I shall know what to do with anyone who's reported to me for behaving badly to our visitors. Shan't I?' He seemed incapable of avoiding these rhetorical inquiries, which produced in the school a tremendous corporate frustration of the wish to reply. Indeed, the hall heaved with what was clearly a resolve to take up the various challenges offered. Could he not see this? The rustle became suddenly, glee-fully loud. 'That will do,' he pronounced. 'I think that will do, won't it?' I thought it was with some haste that he moved on to the final hymn. It was one of which the gist was that the Lord might look down on us throughout the hours that followed, confident that he'd find us straining to follow a path of quite exceptional rectitude. Baynes and I exchanged gloomy glances.

'Damn this unadventurous educational system with its well-meaning grey soul,' growled my diary.

It was a curious teaching practice: in a dulled school, but an anxiously decent one. In general, a kind of immensely lack-lustre decency—that was the quality of it. Our visiting tutor was Mr Potton, whose lack of all flair for paperwork meant that some visits did not (to use his own blushing verb) materialise. It might be said, I think, that we were supervising Mr Potton rather than the other way round: for in our most significant encounter we blundered into him in a local café, to find him carrying his lunch on a tray; and we saw at once that this meal did not begin to exhibit that range of *colour* that, according to one of his own lectures, should be the mark of our own and our pupils' lunches. It was most awfully yellow and red, and shockingly short on green.

I enjoyed being with Baynes: he was a sensible, resourceful teacher, who held that he was at ease because these boys were exactly like the boy he'd been himself. He'd come from a similar district, close at hand. Awfully difficult to dig yourself out of such places, he said. Slums and near-slums. He'd managed it himself, with the help of an energetic wife—was living now in a politer outer suburb: and was about to launch a campaign to rescue his younger brother. 'I have to get him out before he gets used to it—then *nothing* will get him out.' It was talk about prisons and prison camps—but the subject was the inner suburbs of London.

Baynes put me at ease about an incident that occurred on our second day, and would have had, to my eyes—without his guidance—all the marks of shocking melodrama. A Mrs Seaman arrived to make complaints about the treatment of her son. She didn't go to the Head's room, she didn't ask to see anyone—she simply wandered through the building, orating. She filled the hall, the whole school, with bright mockery. 'Well, I dunno who's responsible for it, but my boy's fed up to the back teeth with being here. Some boys they have a down on. That's teachers for you.' She addressed this opinion at a sidling group of fourth years, who guffawed bashfully. Well, she stood arms akimbo, her body on display, its major features as heavily stressed as if they'd been accompanied by that device they use in comics—the radiating, ejaculating lines that mean a bump raised on the head, an aching bottom. As she drifted through the hall, up and down corridors, I caught sight of the Head, scuttling away in the distance, trying to find someone who'd remove her from the scene. She opened a classroom door and shouted, not unamiably: 'My boy don't like this place!'

Baynes pointed the boy out to me. Seaman, he said, didn't like or dislike anything. Inside him was total indifference. He responded to his mother's performance with grinning apathy; I didn't know then how many faces like his I was to meet in the years of teaching to come, their grins a mark for total inner numbness.

I asked Baynes to come in and listen to my teaching. He was

amused at my attempts at fierceness. 'Wouldn't at all mind having terrible things said to me by you,' he remarked. 'You make them sound so nice.' It seemed the equivalent of saying that no boy could do other than welcome the idea of meeting me in a dark alley. Having sent their children into hysterics by threatening them with a policeman, mothers could restore them to good humour by threatening them with me. And so on. I was also too refined, said Baynes. 'You speak to them, you know, as if you were speaking to colleagues in the staffroom. Very funny.'

I didn't see the joke. So short of ordinary ogreishness and common or garden coarseness, how could I ever become a teacher?

5

But the joy of that last practice, the unexpected bonus, was the luck I had in working with a teacher called Buller.

I hadn't at all liked him on my preliminary visit. He would, he said firmly, stay in the room while I taught. My optional subject was English? Then he very much hoped I *liked* English. Keen on versemaking, himself: approached it through a discussion of the technicalities. 'Why deprive them of knowing about spondees and dactyls and trochees?' My heart sank. How could this happen so blatantly in an English classroom, when no man in a room where Art was taught, in such a school, would dream of approaching the work through a discussion of chiaroscuro and tempera and basso relievo? Buller, like the Head, seemed to assume that I had no ideas of my own. Of course I was the student and he was the veteran. But should he not, out of ordinary courtesy, have asked me how *I* would approach verse-making in the classroom?

And when the experience began, how different he was! Or

rather, how very much the same! The difference lay in my understanding of him. Buller was the first magically gifted *conservative* teacher I'd ever observed. He was tall, in a rather helpless way: that is, his limbs seemed to have grown longer than he'd ever intended, and there were parts of them he appeared never to have claimed. So his trousers, and the sleeves of his jacket, were distinctly too short. There was a clumsy impression of wrists and ankles he'd not consented to cover. His face, like his name, was that of some nineteenth century field-marshal, a hawk's face, complete with a moustache that was a sort of military encampment on that large, eventful, war-like surface. But look twice, and you saw humour and subtlety, the possibility of deep and unusual smiles.

Buller taught hard: gently and humorously so. His class, of last year boys, was relaxed: I was later to realise, remarkably relaxed. 'Don't,' Buller warned me, 'regard this as a magic phenomenon: it's based on old struggles.' He was, among other things, always in the room. It was not characteristic of this school: it was not, I was to discover, characteristic of many schools. The rule was, for example, that during any break boys must be in the playground, unless there was a master in their classroom. All teachers but Buller dashed to the staff room: it was where they yearned to be. Buller stayed among the boys. Partly this may have been because an old pupil had gone to work in a famous brewery, which had the practice of sending a pot of yeast, free, weekly, to any who wished to receive it. Buller was addicted to yeast. The eating of it marks the breath, very strongly —merely opening the lid on a potful causes an exhalation not to everyone's taste. At some time or other I think Buller might have been advised that he was—he and his pot of yeast were—not welcome in the staffroom. But I think he might have stuck to his classroom, anyway. He had introduced a comfortable armchair into it, surely not official issue, and there he sat, at playtimes and dinnertimes and for a while after school, a field-marshal converted into a squire, with boys milling round. One cause of their being present was the current collection of books that lay scattered about the place. Buller was always introducing books into the room, and then taking them away again. This was the only school I was ever in where a boy, a particularly unlikely lad, cried out: 'Where's that *Compleat Angler*, then?' Buller had bought a copy of Walton's classic at a local secondhand book-shop, and left it around for a week before taking it home—too soon for the angler who raised the cry. 'Don't think he's ever caught more than a tiddler,' said Buller, 'but you see how grieved he is.' Then, raising his voice : 'I'll bring it back on . . . Thursday, Mick. Can you wait till Thursday?' Mick grinned : 'All right, sir—Thursday, then.' Did Buller's boys understand how he, a pedagogic Isaak Walton, fished for their moments of interest, the points at which they were vulnerable to his hooks and worms? I realised, watching Buller, that the answer to such a question didn't matter. He *cared* about them—that's all they knew : and it was all they needed to know. To land Mick at a moment when he had some interest in a book, Buller would have stolen, I believe, a first edition of Isaak Walton from the British Museum, if necessary.

Buller, in fact, was a conservative who'd have engaged in crime, anarchy, all sorts of unrespectability and (he would have said) 'mere socialism' to secure the interest of his boys. 'This is the atmosphere I like to create for them—like a common room,' he told me once when morning school was over, and boys were wandering about the room, talking. And on the same occasion : 'I like the atmosphere to be as like that of a home as possible.' Buller was, after all, no gentleman engaged in slumming—talking airily of common rooms. The common room was a home.

Early on during that practice I took, in his presence, a lesson on current affairs. He sat writing while I talked, much too much —and with none of his ability to command their thoughtful response—of the outside world, as if it were inexorably outside, and foreign to them. I was ashamed as I did so. Buller's gift was to relate anything, almost any subject matter, the world's grandest affairs, to his rough-and-ready fourteen-year-olds. I think it was, at the end of my awkward performance, a silent lesson, for my benefit, when he took from a boy a *Daily Mirror* and asked him, gently, what he read it for. He turned the pages as he asked his question. 'Why do you read a newspaper then, Fred?' Fred shrugged and groaned with his sense of the impossibility of answering this immense question. All the same, since old Buller asked it, he brought his attention to the elusive, hopeless idea of an answer. What struck me specially was that Buller gave no hint that he himself was a non-*Mirror* reader. Conservative, gentlemanly, he totally lacked condescension.

As for me, I realised that I had been talking to the class exactly as if they'd been readers of *The Times*.

Oh God, staffrooms . . . The one at Cannon Road was a glorified cloakroom with primitive provisions for refreshment, to which you might bring at most a pile of exercise books. Noisy. Hideously overcrowded.

True that at times comfort was to be drawn from the massive presence of colleagues. Being alone with children for hours on end sometimes made the mere company of adults, even in a large muddled crowd, intensely welcome. But if childish noise and bustle made you long at times for adult noise and bustle, one or both of them, in a cramped school, could create an enormous desire for mere silence. That was when your teacher's headache came : a hammering in the skull caused by the impossibility of ever escaping from an insistent crush of children alternated with an insistent crush of adults.

Doubly welcome to be able to stay, some days, with Buller in his room, among his surprising, quietly talking boys . . .

By much staffroom conversation I was reminded of the way my mother had edited the facts of her daily life, restoring herself to the centre of them. 'So I told her . . .' mother would innocently assert, 'She'd never thought of that . . .' : 'I put her in her place.' You'd been with her and knew that mother had listened most patiently, nodding eager agreement . . . Teachers, talking of their encounters with children, tended to use the same dramatic device. 'Well, I said there was only one answer to that, and I gave it to them . . . They were dead silent. Dead silent ! Not a sound from them for the rest of the lesson.' 'I told them what I thought about that, and you could see it went home. I don't think they'll do that again.'

It was, alas, most of it, self-deceiving. They hadn't been dead silent. It hadn't gone home. They most certainly would do it again.

Sometimes it seemed part of a conspiracy to pretend that teaching was simple. If there were difficulties, they arose from exceptional failures of personality, and were really not to be much talked of. There was this habit of glossing over the problems. Partly, as I already knew from painful experience, it was because the value of a teacher's personality did indeed seem to be at stake. How easy to feel that failing at first to teach in any satisfactory fashion proved there was in you some deep and incurable deficiency . . .

So in many teachers—as a result of first experiences, and this general custom of silence about difficulties—was implanted the habit of pretending that all was well, even when it plainly was not. I was beginning to long for someone to admit to awkwardnesses, headaches. Even Buller, anxious that I shouldn't believe the happy orderliness of his class was easily created, didn't quite come out with the assertion I'd have been so glad to hear: that there was absolutely no disgrace in taking your time to grow into this subtle, perplexing job.

The Head meanwhile captured me on every possible occasion, and offered me the benefit of . . . everything but his educational experience. So he would talk about how he'd built his own house, and how much it cost, and the current bills he had to pay, and of the excellence of the school under his leadership, and of the remarkable qualities he'd had when a mere teacher, and how his son was at Oxford, and studied Greek, and would have made the ancient Greeks pant rather, trying to keep up with him linguistically. There was one awful afternoon almost wholly devoured by a monologue in which the Head informed me of the profound scorn he had for those who talked of nothing but themselves.

Buller taught music: which, for some reason, required at Cannon Road that he take his piano with him from classroom to classroom. It was about this time that I decided that the mere amount of internal travel school buildings could impose on teachers and children was scarcely rational. There were times of the day when we were all in struggling transit. Being Buller, he'd organised this musical traffic in a cheerful fashion, and there were boys, I guessed, who came to school primarily in order to push old Buller's piano. You'd run into it in corridors, buoyantly and sometimes songfully being wheeled from room to room, with some exceedingly self-important crew in charge. I sat in on a number of Buller's music lessons. 'Right,' he'd say, from the piano, 'we'll break the silence with beautiful sounds . . . eh?

That's the way to begin singing.' Curiously often this was the prelude to just such a breach of the silence: with words, and personal warmth, and a kind of business-like ardour, Buller could command beautiful sounds. There was a class once, on a cloudy and generally bedraggled afternoon, who made a sound that was like the singing of thirty-six persons thickly gagged. 'Ah,' said Buller. '*No!* Imagine there's a man inside your mouth, and that your mouth is a cave! Now, if the man runs back into the cave, you can't hear him . . . Eh?' The next sounds from the class, on that sullen afternoon, were as clear and forward as if it had been the happiest of days.

And once we were with 3D, who were awfully backward, and most of them unable to read. They sang 'Robin Adair', and it might have been any song—any un-song. 'Aaah!' said Buller, and lowered his head onto the keyboard, which caused a challenging jangle. 'Aaah! Well, I'm going to ask my friend if he understood the story you were telling him in that song. He has come . . . oh, many miles to hear that story.' To me: 'Did you understand it? There's no point in singing it if no one can understand it, is there?' The target suddenly of many anxious glances, I blushed and spread out my hands, noncommittally. '*Who's* it all about?' Buller demanded. He made a gobbling attempt, like their own, at the name: Robin Adair. They corrected him, with sudden unnerving accuracy. He spoke line by line, in their style, as gibberish. They put him right, with the clarity of BBC announcers. 'Understand it?' he called in my direction. 'Perfectly,' I said. The class and I directed delighted grins at that obtuse, half-deaf friend of ours, the absurd and wonderful Mr Buller.

I came in one morning and thought I was in the wrong room. There was an ashen silence: Buller was pacing up and down, unsmiling. His form was sitting so still it might have been dead: whenever Buller halted in his pacing, it became improbably stiller. 'And Jenkins,' said Buller, to a boy he'd never in my hearing called anything but Jack, 'your face is *not* clean. I doubt very much if you've washed this morning. You may remember one of my rules about that?' 'You don't have people in the room who haven't washed,' mumbled Jenkins. 'Don't care for mumbling,' said Buller coldly. 'Would you like to say that again?' The woebegone Jack said it again, as audible as a leading actor. Then he left the room, bound for a washbasin.

I stood petrified myself while Buller visited his icy dissatisfaction on one boy after another. It was as if the sky had fallen. Even when angry, Buller was unfailingly courteous : but it was a courtesy that cut like a knife. Rudeness might have been much more comfortable . . . I was wondering about the cause of it all when I found Buller at my side. He turned his back on the class and whispered : 'They *are* good lads, aren't they ! I've been very lucky, you know. I've had some good forms but this one would take some beating . . . We need to tighten up now and then. Does us all good. I do this once or twice a term. I'll let them have another few minutes of it, and then you can give them that lesson you've prepared. Shall I look at your notes?'

It was a lesson on how to calculate the volume of a cone. My notes were marked by the usual squeamish division of the topic into passages timed with absurd exactitude, and by the usual nervous attempt to conform to the sequence of steps laid down, as essential for those acquiring knowledge, by Johann Friedrich Herbart: Preparation, Presentation, Formulation and Application. Buller looked up expressionless from the notebook, but I could guess at the steps his own thoughts had been following : Diversion, Rejection, Polite Dissimulation. Then he called for a boy to fetch, from a cupboard, an assortment of wooden solids. The class warily returned to life. 'I shouldn't, you know,' said Buller, 'bother with your notes. Why not just talk round these things?' I was amazed by them—I'd not seen such a set since we'd used one at school, nearly twenty years before, as the material of drawing lessons. I knew how to give a sketch of a cone some faintly plausible quality of roundedness : but, mathematically, its transformation from an abstract object to a real one threw me. I was even more cruelly thrown by the various cubes, cylinders, pyramids and spheres. Mercifully, Buller himself took part in the lesson : he could sense where a gap began to yawn in my maths, and did not leave it yawning. 'I enjoyed that,' I told him afterwards. 'Learned a lot.' 'They did, too,' he said, grinning. Then he added words that, when I really began to teach, I was always recalling. 'What matters, you know,' he said, 'is not "*What* shall I teach?" What matters is " Shall I *teach*?" '

6

Back at the flat, our mad little son, uttering his weird cries and making his weirder faces. There was a letter from the London County Council: my starting salary would be £381. It was less than my training grant.

I felt trapped in boxes: the tiny immediate one of school practice, inside the rather larger one of the college, inside the box, larger still—large as a working lifetime—of the teaching profession. Oh, ample enough, but still a box: a square black form of captivity, sealed in every direction.

It was May—and suddenly hot. We walked Tom down the road, bosomy with flowering chestnuts, and into the town. He had found his feet, and lay in his pram clutching them, like some complacent little acrobat. Then he blinked and laughed and wept bitterly as blizzards of mayblossom fell upon him . . .

Would teaching be as tiring as this, for more than thirty years to come? I was, so often, in that condition when your face seems fixed in a mad frown behind which your normal, unfrowning, unstartled thoughts seem absolutely out of place.

Buller was marvellous, but the Head . . . so grotesque. I had begun to hate the actual shortness of his jacket. It made his bottom, in shining blue cloth, as much a point of identity as his face. I had at times the mad wish to bend down and speak to it. His performance at morning assembly was that of some boringly depressed prophet. 'If things go on like this,' he'd say, when nothing worse had happened than a boy grinning during a hymn, 'then it's going to be the most unsuccessful term we've ever had.' It was a worried mannerism: he had no gift for cheerful statement because, I believe, he was always afraid that any let-up on his expectation of the worst could lead to . . . oh, perhaps the actual collapse of the school building. He was a little rattle of a man, basically good-natured, who was everlastingly anxious to do well. Was it his character that gave the school its atmosphere of worried smallness of mind? Buller apart, there was so much anxiety about, attached to so much morose attention to, surely unimportant, detail.

'May I say . . .?' the Head asked, at assembly. The school did not refuse its permission : it shrugged its corporate shoulders. 'I should like,' he said, after a master had described a game of football played the previous evening, 'to add a word *thereunto*—' He presided over an Empire Day service totally unrelated to political or moral reality. It was rather as though all those taking part had gone quite mad. The Head made a speech that for its flagwaving naïvety would have brought a blush to the cheeks of Cecil Rhodes in 1890. There was only one word for it all : insincere. There, curiously, wasn't a shred of sincerity in any of it. And that did seem odd, as part of the proceedings of a school . . .

I was constantly being pushed in a mathematical direction. It led to my being closeted one afternoon with 3B and one of the worst of textbooks. 'Let them get on with Exercise 1,753,' their usual master seemed to advise me. It turned out to feature improbable manoeuvres with fractions. Would anyone in any actual situation as experienced by living human beings attempt to resolve such a relationship as was implied by the notation :

$$\frac{476}{703} \times \frac{2227}{1539} \div \frac{152}{969} \times \frac{2299}{1819} \ ?$$

I think not. But, on an afternoon I shall never forget, 3B and I set out on the attempt. The secret, I should say at once—if it counts as a secret—is that the calculation presents no problem to anyone far-sighted enough to have mastered the 17 and 19 times tables. We'd all, as it happened, halted at the 12 times table. 3B weren't bad at that. I thought it was cruel to deprive them of the comfort of such facility as they had. It was crueller still to deprive me of it. They all groaned over this sum. 'Sir!' *'Sir!'* Cries of anger from all corners. Foolishly, this brought out in me not only a desire to give comfort, but also a belief that I knew *how* to give it. So I set the sum out on the blackboard gallantly, with a clatter of chalk like the clicking of military heels : and then I began (this I understood very much later) with a simple cancellation that happened to be wrong. It could not have been more wrong. I had allowed the blood of a sort of gallantry to rush to my brain, and it had led to a fatal illusion.

Years later, at home in a classroom, I'd have admitted quite early on that I was in some sort of trap, and might as well, having said so, step out of it. As a teacher-in-training, my only certainty was that I must make no such admission. A teacher must be infallible. The admission of fallibility would lead to rioting . . . I pressed on. The first illusion led to others : to fantasies of cancellation that carried the sum across the blackboard, and down it, and so, for perhaps a quarter of an hour, onwards : with the class, at first on my side out of some sense that I was indeed to be their rescuer, becoming quite wildly hostile. Well, they had found that sum difficult : but here was an apparent teacher who was finding it—oh, some such phrase as 'transcendentally impossible'.

I remember the boy who cried in the end : 'Oh, give up, sir— *give up*! You must have gone wrong somewhere!' Their anger was mixed with pity. The bell went before we'd got beyond this phase: on their part, psychiatric. They didn't want me to leave the room quite deranged. 'Ah, forget it, sir,' said a boy, as I struggled among them to reach the door. 'They're all like that. Only worse,' he added, enigmatically. I was not at the time able to appreciate the splendid nature of this statement : which implied that I'd been in trouble only on the lower slopes of these ridiculous Everests of arithmetic.

But I shouldn't have been in trouble at all. I was a teacher— in intent, anyway. I felt like a magician who'd turned out to be totally unfamiliar with rabbits and doves. Never seen a rabbit or a dove in his life!

I couldn't tell Kate about it. She merely said, that evening, and most mildly, that I was perhaps in danger of removing all romance from our embraces, by establishing and then adhering to the convention that she was always the attacker, and I always the innocent victim of *her* inordinate lust.

'Sometimes, honestly,' she said, 'I do wonder—oh, you mustn't feel you have to tell me—but I do wonder what has happened during the day, to bring on these—'

I ruined her sentence with disgraceful pressures—designed, I told myself guiltily, to blot out for a moment my consciousness of being absolutely, *criminally*, ignorant of the 17 and 19 times tables.

7

. . . and boredom. Well, it was something even the realistic Mr Jepp never dealt with : the inescapable boredoms of teaching. They could come from the experience of working, day after day, within a tightly closed community, furiously and complicatedly —or even, as was the case with Cannon Road, sluggishly— active. The sheer physical dullness of school buildings could be a cause : a sudden weariness with the petty routine that's part of the life of any school, and of a school like this one, a large part. Of course, any occupation has its tedious moments : but they seemed worse in teaching because the general idea about teaching was that it ought to be lively. And the boredom of the teacher sometimes looked worse because it was so obviously out of key with the juvenile vivacity of his classes.

Well, I thought being bored was a sort of treason. It was certainly terribly easy to be bored, in Cannon Road. It was a topic that I wished Mr Jepp had been honest with us about.

And fatigue, of course. All that division of attention. All that need to dominate. The hundred voices a teacher must have— sometimes many voices at one and the same time. The constant need to explain, and to make clear. How often I longed to leave some point lost in a vague, smiling mumble . . . And the terrible subdivision of the day, in terms of place as well as time. You were always darting about. It was always 2.15 when you thought it was 3.45.

But I had a break from boredom, if not from fatigue, when Buller said : 'They're short at the girls. Would it interest you to go across and take a class? You don't have to, of course. It'd be perfectly understood if you refused. But if you've never taken girls, it might be . . . a useful experience.'

I didn't in the least want to do it, but hadn't the courage to return a cowardly 'No.' So I walked from the growling boys' building across the playground to the girls', which seemed to giggle. I felt at once like someone involved in a farce. There were girls doing P.E. in the hall as I walked across it—a blurred fantasy, in my vision, of tall creatures, all tee-heeing, and all unbelievably long of leg. I felt my face flaming, and tried miserably to think myself into the state of mind of a legitimate professional visitor. In an episode of which I seemed unable to grasp the details, I inquired for the headmistress. Her deputy appeared, a small woman who said you'd have thought they could do better than send a student over. She seemed to be asking me to endorse her view that students were worse than useless. I grinned helplessly. Then I was in a classroom very full indeed of girls, who were fixing me with shameless eyes. 'He's lovely,' said the nearest to the next nearest, who was not quite of her opinion : 'Looks daft.' I was under discussion generally for a buzzing moment. 'Very well,' I said. ' I'm going to read to you.' A girl near the front gave a cry so plausibly horrified that I thought I must have said something quite different. There was more discussion, out of which emerged an agreement that I should provide an example of the activity I'd proposed, after which they would have more to say.

I had with me a book of short pieces by Mark Twain. The one that, by nervous accident, I set about reading was on the writing of love letters. It produced a stunned silence . . . and then willingness to listen, it appeared, to anything I cared to read. It was, I think, the idea of a blushing young learner-teacher from the other world, the men's world, on this site where boys and girls were so adamantly segregated—it was the idea of such a visitor risking everything by the introduction of such a theme that won the day for me. Or the half hour, I should honestly say. Somehow, between us, Mark Twain and I won what I must call an adoring silence from, I'd guess, thirty out of thirty-five girls from that stormy inner suburb (where, Baynes once said, even original sin was second-hand), on that surprising afternoon when their expectation had been that they'd reduce me to blushing tears. *My* expectation had been less precise, but I'd certainly expected disaster.

Buller listened to my story, and said he hoped I wouldn't think it indelicate if he suggested that it had all the misleading marks of a honeymoon.

'Well, you know what he meant by that,' said Kate.

Ben had warned us about honeymoons. Their own had been a nightmare, he said, as any encounter of an intimate kind between two unqualified, untrained youngsters must be. (It was back to lesson notes, I thought.) Ben had been bolder with women, during the war, than I'd been. But I'd had a glimpse of the limits of this boldness when he said once that he thought he was made of baser metal than me. 'I can't imagine you taking girls out, as I do—fondling their arms . . .'

My God! *Fondling their arms!*

'I suppose I've been lucky that some slut hasn't taken me the whole way. But it's fear, of course. Fear of VD. And fear of not knowing what to do. Any young man's fear, I guess, of making a fool of himself.'

Well, Kate and I, uncertified lovers, had had this exceedingly brief honeymoon, an autumn half-term long, in Cambridge. We were both unfamiliar with hotels, and I found the business of introducing us into one, and dealing at the same time with the novelty of our married status, almost unbearable. As we climbed the stairs to our bridal chamber, the entire hotel seemed to snigger. Informed below of the possibility of fun, as I paranoiacally believed, a chambermaid had dashed up ahead of us, to watch me fumble with the door key as if I'd never unlocked anything in my life before. Then Kate and I were alone. I was worried by a nuance as of this being a penalty rather than a privilege, until I realised that the tiny hotel room had the character of a prison cell.

And I had the 'flu. Unmistakably, expungingly, a trembling, wan 'flu.

It was November, Guy Fawkes time. The pallor of the buildings was a solid form of the drifting pallor of mist. Red heaps of leaf underfoot, and the trees starred with the last golden clusters. Gold and silver: leaves and mist. Students, but then the word was undergraduates, were collecting money for Poppy Day. On

158

Parker's Piece, the matador Il Statu Pupillari fought the bull Il Proctoro Furioso. Six aristos were guillotined at Trinity Gate. Miles of pennies stretched along the pavements. And Kate was fined for her New Look. It was her wedding coat, brown corduroy, down to the ground, a tube inside which she experienced, I think, something like total sartorial amazement. Coming down the stairs on buses I had to walk behind her, holding her train clear . . .

And back in the hotel, there was something wrong with our lesson notes. Or was it my cold, perhaps, so ungenerously timed? We laughed helplessly, our erotic tactics having so much of the study about them, the novice's textbook naughtiness. Those lovings during our courting—rather approximate, incomplete. Concert performance was to come . . .

In the end, sleep, hand in hand, seemed almost as good as anything. We having been warned, after all, about honeymoons . . .

Oh all these courtings and wooings, of wives and occupations —this general state of uneasy honeymoon!

It was like the end of other school practices. I was beginning to love the hated school. I found myself fond of the intolerable well-meaning Head. He showed me the report he was sending to Isleden ('Do *not* allow the student to see this', I read). I was courteous and co-operative: I had very good control of a class. Under Special Abilities the Head had written: 'Command of English'. 'Well,' he said, 'I've enjoyed our conversations.'

Buller suggested I use my last hour with his class ('Oral Composition' said his timetable) by talking about myself and getting them to tell me about themselves. We drew Buller in, finally, and he told us about himself. 'You can let them know now,' said Buller, 'the word for all this . . . You remember, you were going to tell them at the beginning. But I think it's better this way round.'

'It's called autobiography,' I said, bashfully.

8

It became tremendously hot. We woke sweating, to air already painfully bright. The heat made itself felt as a positive pressure: one was being leaned on by it. We walked about like dazzled snails.

And, now we were back at Isleden, the course began to die under a great weight of obsequies. We did nothing in various wearying forms. There was the mounting of an exhibition. It was what Isleden had always been best at. Op Geog had made a relief model of the surrounding patch of London, too big ever to leave the room it was built in. Op Maths had constructed eye-deceiving solids, mobile graphs, machines that reinforced learning with bells or trumpets—or, on Open Day, in the case of one malfunctioning invention, volleys of flatulence. Op Sci had caught the essence of Einstein in cardboard. The college buffoons converted their own persons into models and visual aids: the corridors were crammed with simultaneous equations on the move, leggy rhombohedrons.

I walked nervously into the Op Lit room and deposited there an essay on John Donne's *Anniversaries*—handbound, with nauseously marbled covers.

There were many forms to fill in: among them, one in which we were asked to set down our intentions in respect of the two years course of study we were required to follow after training had finished. Mr Trellis came into hall angrily grasping a fistful of these forms. Some characters, he snapped, with security reached, were proving *brittle*. The forms, in a *shockingly* large number of cases, were most *unsatisfactorily* filled in. He could only suggest to the men responsible that they should *pull their socks up*. Several highflying students in the front row were seen nervously doing this. Mr Trellis's lectures on philosophical idealism had left us all uneasy about the connection between any

160

image he might use, and reality, and some indeed found it hard to shake off the idea that, unless Mr Trellis was actually observing them, they were not wearing socks at all—or, come to that, anything else.

The longest possible series of last days began—incompletely attended. There were fitful drama festivals, and outbursts of choral verse speaking, and the photographic society photographed absolutely everything, and the fencers fought each other to a standstill and then began all over again, and Capper was in the gym from morning to late afternoon, defending against all comers his supremacy in various brutal fields.

Meanwhile, behind office doors, the winding up of our affairs was understood to be going grimly on.

There was a service of dedication. We were asking for blessings on our vocation. An actual great purple butterfly of a bishop presided, a man who gave the frightening impression of being able to pray, and later to talk, for ever. His voice had a steady underlying purr to it, as if electricity was involved. He took a view of history against which our History lecturer, Mr Strike, had often warned us. It was the view that great events or movements were exclusively products of the lives of great men. 'Had not,' the bishop hummed, 'a dissatisfied painter named Schickelgruber become interested in politics, the last war would not have occurred.' Mr Strike, sitting quite close at hand, smiled aimlessly and nodded. A few minutes later the bishop was saying: 'Had not a disgruntled German sat for hours in the British Museum writing a diatribe against the wealthy, there would have been no communism.' This time, Mr Strike's dishonest smile came into conflict with a marxist hiss from the back of the hall. The bishop completed a rather long sequence of the kind with the opinion, difficult to resist, that if there had been no war, there would have been no emergency training scheme: and that this in its turn would have led to a quite conspicuous absence of emergency trained teachers.

This was followed by a more secular occasion, the ceremony of closure, attended by the Minister of Education himself. Mr Trellis, gowned and hooded, was the first speechmaker. His address had the usual characteristics—such large hopefulnesses expressed in language so nobly overdressed—but it suddenly changed: *he* changed: he paused and grew red and then spoke

161

in a new voice about his disgust, there being half the staff and over thirty students not yet placed or replaced in schools. It was startling, and moving. I wished there had been earlier occasions of anger from Mr Trellis. Was that sonorous idealism merely a blanket under which all sorts of interesting furies lay smothered? The angry passage left his brow red, but he had returned by the end to his familiar style. 'Isleden's harpstrings are broken,' he informed the Minister, 'but her music may well be eternal.'

The Minister, one felt, could have taken in his stride any sudden passion on the part of any principal of a training college about to expire. He had a charm of his own with which to counter Mr Trellis's boyish charm. He smiled at Mr Trellis: he picked up the principal's reference to Isleden's possible musical immortality and assented to it, but with a smiling briskness, expressed in a north country voice, that somehow converted a mildly absurd assertion into a fairly practical one. One imagined him back at the Ministry, translating Mr Trellis's aspiration into a statistic. 'Training colleges wishing their music to be eternal, former, 1'. He spoke with a kind of light heaviness. You couldn't say it was a frivolous speech, but you couldn't say it was a serious one, either. It left the sincere and the insincere equally cheated. The Minister had physical mannerisms agreeable to watch. Plump, with the general air of some shrewd baby, he made his hands dance, he set his head at various angles, and he operated a laundry: that's to say, he'd present an idea (not much of an idea) as if it were some item of clothing, plunge it into a bowl, scrub at it and then wring it, and, after a pantomime of rinsing, drop the thing on some virtually visible draining board before taking up the next. It was as though, I thought, his body had adapted itself entirely to the need for oratorical effect. Could he ever say anything to anybody about anything without those overtones of the washhouse?

To Mr Trellis's angers he made no reply. Yet he somehow contrived to suggest that an answer had been not so much given as creatively withheld. He seemed to have the gift of making dissatisfaction itself, satisfactory.

I thought he was a charmer. Such an amiable display! I confessed this to Bing and Broom, who sighed, in chorus, for perhaps the last time. 'He is an old political whore,' said Bing, speaking with friendly slowness and severity. 'That's how they obtain

162

power and then hold on to it,' explained Broom. 'By charming the gullible.'

Oh blast, I thought. Thirteen months of Isleden and I was still helplessly among the gullible. There was in me such a childish longing that people should be what they seemed to be.

And so to the actual last day. Certificates, which defied anyone to quarrel with our status as positive teachers, and testimonials were distributed. The latter were stereotyped documents into which individual details had been inserted, and offered a nice field for comparative interpretation. 'Very good' seemed to be a phrase representing a tepid contentment on the part of the authorities: a respectable pass. Bing and Broom and I had this applied to our general college work and our teaching. Capper, discovering that his work in college was derided as 'Good', wanted to challenge Mr Trellis, or Mr Trellis and Mr Jepp together, to innumerable rounds with the gloves in the gym. 'Excellent' was clearly a cut above 'Very good'—in this curious code of approvals and disapprovals, it suggested a certain animation, an approach to enthusiasm. It was applied to my optional work. I was, the document asserted, 'an excellent actor', prone to give 'polished portrayals'. Bing suggested that 'polished' might be among these words with their subtle shades of praise or dispraise, so that my portrayals might not be quite in the same class as, say, 'burnished portrayals'. But we were unable to check on this. My character was summed up as 'very pleasant, gentlemanly'—Bing and Broom exchanged political glances—'unassuming, but capable, co-operative and efficient'. I took it that the use of 'but' after 'pleasant, gentlemanly and unassuming' suggested some dissatisfaction with those qualities.

We gave Mr Salt a book token, an action which made it necessary for him to secure himself to the face of the earth by grasping assorted doorknobs, light fittings and items of furniture. There was then a special grand dinner. This turned out to be one in which the appalling qualities of Isleden cooking were vastly exaggerated and, on the whole, smothered under a deeply false sort of cream.

And Bing and Broom and I stood outside the underground station, before our final parting, and talked about the latest threat to all our plans. It was taking place in . . . oh, Korea.

PART FOUR

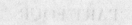

1

It was the next day: we had turned from insubstantial students to solid teachers without a pause. In a cellar, a score of men from Isleden. I was reminded of a scene from some early film about abject forms of employment. We swarmed round an official, who plucked, for some, jobs out of the air. Having had that primary emphasis was best. 'What is it you want?' he asked, as if any answer I gave must be grossly unreasonable. 'Senior?' He turned to share a desperate grimace with his desk. 'I've got nothing for you now—but I'll see what can be done.'

There were four weeks till the end of summer term. Some students had entered into furtive agreements with teaching practice schools, and had been actually asked for. They left the cellar at once, struggling to overlay delight with a little decent shame. The rest of us were supernumeraries.

From insubstantial students, without a pause, to insubstantial supernumeraries . . .

Halfway through the morning, Kingsbury Central rang. They had a man away, sick. Anyone hanging about the office? The official groaned. 'You can have half a dozen.' He picked me. 'It's a decent school. You're lucky.'

1930ish building, airy enough. I was sent in, post haste, to 3 Alpha: who, having so far had a riotously unsupervised morning, would have made light work of a squad of commandoes. 'Take the relative pronoun,' I'd been advised. 'They can always do with that.' I took it, or attempted to take it: and they made it clear that they had rather often done with it. Much of its natural glamour had seeped out of it. Here I was, a total stranger, face to face with thirty total strangers, and we sought to anchor our relationship instantly to the relative pronoun. It made neither educational nor social sense.

167

I ran the gauntlet of classes who saw me as the most trumpery and anonymous of stand-ins. I imagined that they took me to be a supply teacher, one of those peripatetics called upon when teachers were sick : professionally faceless. That sort of teaching, I thought, my head aching, was for the profoundly seasoned, the very oldest professional hickory, and not at all for the beginner.

But no, as it turned out I did not even create an illusion of being one of these educational nomads. 'That *student*,' said a boy, unerringly. From insubstantial student, without a pause, to insubstantial student . . .

Kate asked, eyes shining: 'Good day—your first day?' I pointed out to her that we were being watched. Behind the trees lining the cricketfield a preposterous golden moon, surely having arrived too early, was lurking, with a real effect of clumsy slyness. 'It was a bad day,' said Kate, translating, and sighed.

Oh the misery of it ! If I'd not had wife and child to provide for, I'd have run. It was like being a teacherly version of the Dutch boy who kept the sea away with a finger in the dyke. A hole would open up in Kingsbury's timetable and I'd be rushed in with my finger. Much of the sea seemed to get in, just the same. I was floundering about in classroom after classroom, knee-deep in it. In the staffroom I found it unwise to dispose myself in an attitude that could be mistaken for the enjoyment of inactivity. It was so exclusively my character to be horribly occupied that a teacher had only to catch sight of me to be reminded of the instant possibility of yet another form of horrible occupation . . .

Roger Bunce called in at the flat with an unexpected lady. My old friend, after some sort of committee meeting with himself, had proposed that marriage should be aimed at : and there had been a general decision to this effect. Grace was musical. Roger pointed out, on her behalf, that *Tristan and Isolde* was being broadcast that evening, and turned on the wireless at full volume. The enormous music seized us, we were at once in its splendid power : we could not move : we had no conscience. The suburb shook. I half-feared, when it was over, that Mrs Nape might be lying dead below, simply murdered by music. Tom slept through it all : our little Wagner of the belch and the trumpeting yawn, impervious to this other one.

The devil was, again, that I liked the boys who were making

me miserable. And they were hardly to be blamed for what happened. A lesson with a supernumerary was a nothing: an occasion that was connected with no other occasion. If the man was a quivering beginner, why do other than set out to turn his quiver into a quake?

It was the routineer's depression I felt, leaving home in the morning, sitting in the staffroom. On the analogy of the baby-sitter, I was a class-sitter. And I was having ample opportunity to examine the worst of myself, as a teacher. My being basically—and, in a professional sense, ruinously—an indulgent person, for example: who didn't find it easy to bother with rules and regulations. If a boy asked to leave the room, it was my first impulse to believe that he really needed to do so. And it was, alas, my second impulse, too.

I took a vow not to build castles of pessimism on such foundations: and broke this vow daily.

Ben's ascent in the Civil Service had reached the point where he was in charge of a project, and left to manage the affair according to his own unprompted analysis of what was required. 'It's queer,' he said. 'I've never been used to making my own time in my work. There's always been someone to prod me.' It was a matter of a forthcoming census. He was eating, drinking, dreaming census. 'In my dream, everybody in the country gives a false name, and it's my fault because of the way I've framed a question.'

Of course, Ben added, a teacher in his classroom had immense freedom, surely?—Immense freedom, I thought, to drown.

Korea? Well, it was terrible, mad. Yet how dreadful, too, the general resignation to the idea of another global war. Surely nothing could be worse than that? The Russian threat was not bad enough, and what we possessed not good enough, to justify a war?

I was commanded one morning to quit Kingsbury with all haste and go to Savage Street, in the shadow of Kings Cross.

2

Someone once drew what might be called a delinquent map of London's schools, and found that the worst of them followed the main railway lines out of the capital.

Savage Street had a century of soot—Great Northern, and then London North Eastern—in its bricks and stones. You came to it along the dark ugliness of the Hibernian Road, downhill past one of the city's major prisons, and tenements that were tall prisons unscheduled: and so into Savage Street. Little houses with no colour in them anywhere, not even some bright smudge of curtain. Prams containing sooty babies, sucking (though it looked as if they were being sucked by) dummies. A meat stall: hanging joints a strangulated purple, thick in sooty flies.

And the school in the middle, a great horrid thing like something altogether too big to be thrown away.

Up narrow, winding stairs, unwindowed. And so to . . . the very gentlest of headmasters. Courteously he wondered if I'd mind taking 1A, what was left of it: part had gone off on a school journey, which had caused the gaps in the staff that I was to help to fill.

There were nineteen of them: all mine for the next fortnight. My own class, or bit of a class: and my own ring full of keys. Everywhere you went in this school—even to the lavatory—a key was needed. So I had this enormous collection of keys: 'Bluebeard,' I said, introducing myself, and the class grinned with kindly incomprehension.

I was astonished by the depth of the feeling I had about being, even so temporarily, so oddly, a teacher with a patch of territory, an educational fief of his own.

I read them a story, and then went off for the afternoon to

County Hall, where a tea and reception were being given to new entrants to the service.

I guess the practice of providing this occasion had been discussed in terms of humanising an immense educational machine. Little cakes, cups of tea and speeches were to knit us together—with each other, and with our intricate masters. Actually, it reminded me of Sunday School treats I'd been to as a child: it had much of the air of one of these, even to the impression that many kinds of worldly jollity were *not* being emulated. A brisk glumness was the keynote, and was established at the very beginning by a speaker who said that the next time we'd be together would be at the tea party given for *retiring* teachers. I'm not at all sure if it was meant as a joke: I think, in a drab way, it chilled us all.

Bing was there, a supernumerary in South London: and Broom, who'd spent more time in the divisional office, hanging about, than in a school. Capper, rendered almost noiseless by his experience, said he was teaching in a church school, with four teachers, no staffroom, no staff lavatory, leaky ceilings, and an insolent class of all ages from eleven to fifteen. He spent most of *his* time, he said wanly, emptying the buckets that stood all day under the worst drips . . .

They were lively, next morning, little fleas, and unjustly I made that a reason for cancelling their P.E. lesson, which I wasn't keen to take. I didn't want to let them out of the classroom, in which I might hope to create an atmosphere of my own. Set them free, and the atmosphere would belong to Savage Street. Worse—in P.E. it would belong to that terrible playground, its walls growling with obscenities in chalk. And to the girls' school over the way, shrill with a cackling laughter that rose and rang and died and then rose again in some other quarter of the building. A school for young harpies, I thought.

It was a wound, being robbed of P.E., but one that quickly healed. I spent the day getting each character into focus: making sure of names. My boys had names, and I knew them—amazing!

Another ex-student from Isleden arrived. Potts was a doleful man, who believed there was no hope of teaching these boys. They could only be held down, he said. Profoundly mild, he put on a great fierceness when talking of them. 'I'll keep them in their place if it's the last thing I do. They shan't get on top of me.'

As he said this he glared at the boy who'd already made himself my indispensable lieutenant. This was Croucher: whose face was everlastingly red, as with some old fury or shame that had never consented to move on. Because of that angry colour, and his brilliantined spikes of hair, I'd begun by being wary of Croucher, but had discovered that the worst he could do was to break your leg or neck in one of his seizures of helpfulness. When he saw, or thought he saw, that he could be of help, he took off at once, heading for you in immense vague noisy bounds. If he misjudged the distance, there could be collisions. I had learned to hold myself in readiness for one of Croucher's friendly impulses.

'I think,' I said, 'that if a teacher talks to them, interests himself in them, reads to them, and at times talks above their heads, he might have earned his meagre wage.'

'You sound like Mr Trellis,' said Potts, annoyingly.

The staff at Savage Street were given almost to a man to the playing of bridge. This was their consolation for turning up there, day after day. Nothing else ever happened at lunch time: no books were marked, no school matters discussed. There was obsessive bridge. The Head was aloof from it: but then, this gentle man was generally aloof. He sat in his room, reading. The real power was in the hands of the first assistant: a short, squat man who was always making his rounds of the school with angry, pounding steps. He clearly thought he should be in charge of the school, and that the quiet reader in the Head's room was useless, unsuitable, despicably soft. He made it obvious that he expected Potts and me to buckle at once under the strain of teaching—of simply being present—in Savage Street. Now, as we made our way out, at the day's end, he appeared, stepping bitterly, and called across: 'Don't be so cast down.' 'Oh, I'm not cast down,' I cried. 'Far from it. A most interesting day.'

'You sound like Mr Jepp,' said Potts.

3

When, every morning, I passed the prison, I was struck by its resemblance, grimly playful, to the toy fort I'd had as a child.

Kate and I found ourselves often now with noses pressed to shop windows. We were impatient to shower Tom with toys, and so to rediscover them ourselves. I was much in favour of a fort. Exactly like the one I'd had myself : the base being a box in which you kept your soldiers. Lots of blue-uniformed men shouldering the stumps of rifles. And other unforgettable soldiers wearing red, that had rubbed away here and there, on knees and elbows especially, baring plain lead. Silver-patched soldiery. The oblongs they stood on tended to have curled at the corners. Half a moustache would have gone : an eye. The general could review his troops only if there was something against which to lean his three-legged horse. Luckily, he'd lost both eyes, so didn't notice how many Roman legionaries and Arabs and civilians (largely farmers and their bonneted wives) had infiltrated themselves into the force he was to lead against the intrepid, but mostly headless, Sioux.

Your skin was deeply dirty after a day in Savage Street. Ruffett, the first assistant, continued to watch over us with spiteful paternalism. He very much wanted the worst to happen to us. It would probably have happened very quickly to me had half of 1A not been sunning themselves in Swanage. As it was, I had, for a manageable fortnight, my controllable nineteen : and when we were tired I would woo them with a story. I did this in the last lesson of the day : a story by W. W. Jacobs. The bell went but we ignored it. Then came the tattoo of Ruffett's footsteps, the opening of the door and the appearance of his face, maliciously helpful : and everything fell to pieces : for his expectation that I should be a greenhorn made me one.

I hated him for entering my kingdom.

All known, now, my subjects! Walker, who was Croucher's best and worst friend, a stormy boy, ready to quarrel with anybody and anything: Dillamore, slow and thick: and Parrott, who wore an infinitely shabby clerk's black jacket and old pinstriped trousers, and smelt strongly of dog, and had the oddest affection for arithmetic. Giggling Young, in a yellow shirt, never changed, so bright it hurt the eyes: and blunt Coleman, a tiny boy with the oldest of faces: and badly-assembled Russell, who seemed to have many more than the usual number of elbows. I told over their names to myself gratefully: for the first time since I'd left the prep school I had a crew, and a roll to call. Coleman, Croucher, Dillamore, Dodd, Dunkin, Fullagar, Furr; Gladwin, Harris, Massingham, Meek: Munford, Parrott, Pratchett, Price: Russell, Satterthwaite, Walker, Young . . .

Potts was in despair. 'I hate these slum children,' he said, 'who are absolutely ignorant and have such big ideas about themselves.' Yes, of course it was wrong to think of them like that: but—he *loathed* them. Suddenly he sent one of his most difficult boys to me. 'He might do better in your class.' I was angry, having this foreign element introduced: and when I found him spattering Meek with ink, I suddenly seemed to become Potts himself: clipping the boy on the back of the head. I was dismayed by the force and effect of the blow: there were furious tears. Potts came into my room to ask: 'What did you do to him?' Croucher said admiringly: 'Sir sloshed him!' I despised myself for it.

Poor Potts, with his anxious face, his early baldness, his rimless glasses! He was quarterbaked as I was halfbaked. What he really wanted was to go back to Isleden. It had been the happiest year of his life, he said. He'd loved the theoretical air of everything! So many doors opened! The door he was obliged to go through, into teaching, was the one door he'd gladly have left shut.

Ruffett was bitter with disappointed ambition. Of the Head he spoke by way of a special language of disparagement: talking of 'some who make themselves comfortable' or, as he passed you in a corridor, sighing: 'There are those, of course, who, while we labour, sit in the seats of the mighty and . . . read books.' It was the most curious camouflage for his slanders—this pretence that his victim was not one but a whole crowd of headmasters. 'They will need help as usual, I suppose, in keeping order at the end of morning break.' I'd watch him, at assembly, his head bowed, patently brooding over his subordination to a man who could enforce silence only by blowing a whistle.

Ruffett, as he constantly made clear, could keep order without using even words, or movements. He could do it simply by being himself, Ruffett. 'It's years and years of practice. Years and years.' 'That young colleague of yours,' he said, 'seems hardly fit for the profession, eh?' I made the blank face so often necessary when talking to this sour and treacherous man. Indeed, Potts was the noisiest thing in a noisy school. He went into his class in the morning and began roaring and continued to roar all day. Boys flew in and out, dispatched to the Head with demands that he thrash them within an inch of their lives: or simply and aimlessly cast out. 'I believe at times he can't have anyone left in the room,' said Ruffett. I made my blank face.

He wanted us to fail, so much, as a sauce to his own terrible power over the boys. He had the top class, great angry sullen bullies, terrors to all but him. Sometimes he would put on a public display, in hall or corridor, of his capacity simply to gaze these thunderous boys into silence and sheepishness. He'd stump his way round a corner, out of sight, to show that they'd not dare, even then, to stir or speak.

But when he let them go, I'd seen their faces, teeth bared, eyes hot. His control was control by humiliation. They hated him for it.

I wasn't, by any means, in command of my nineteen. They buzzed, they bubbled, they wandered about the room. But we had no terrible quarrels. I was even able, now, to take them into the yard and persuade them to play cricket without turning the game into a long howling dispute. Many of them were masters of ugly argument . . . lived for it. Anger was the air they breathed. I felt it was a triumph of a sort to have them, for half an hour, consenting to overlook the opportunities offered by the gentlemanly game of cricket for almost continuous raucous bickering.

4

Kate, according to Mrs Nape, was scratching our landlady's best furniture. Especially the great mahogany tallboy in our bedroom, built to withstand direct attack by heavy artillery. If Kate had hurled herself at it, scratching and gouging, she'd have had no effect on it whatever. But one Saturday Mrs Nape sent up a note. It said : 'Please take more care of my furniture. There are scratches on the tallboy and I think someone must have been banging on the dressing table with a tin or perhaps trying to cut into it with a knife. Yours faithfully Daisy Nape.' Kate burst into tears, to Tom's great puzzlement. Lying on her lap, he'd been practising his pseudo-language. Lately he'd been specialising in melodious sighs which he brought up from somewhere deep inside himself as if he were trying to refine his voice to a precious essence. It would be, when perfected, an addition to his repertoire of gurgles and whinnies and queer murmurs and squeaks that died away with a comical effect of controlled fading . . .

I went into the bedroom and peered closely at the furniture. If anything it seemed more invulnerably glossy than when I'd last given it any attention.

I did what was, for me, a brave thing. Waiting till Kate and Tom were sharing an afternoon sleep, I went down and bearded Mrs Nape in her den. I do not attempt to refresh this cliché because, applied to Mrs Nape, it is no cliché at all. I suddenly disliked her so much that I was pitilessly aware of the hairiness of her face. Her sitting room had something about it that reminded me of bears. There were no bones in corners, but a feeling that there recently might have been. Much seemed to be of fur, a chair being upholstered in it, and one picture, of an angel appearing to be dancing on hot bricks, was framed in fur.

I informed Mrs Nape that her tallboy and dressing table were both unmarked, and that even if they had been smashed with an axe it would not have been the work of my wife, a woman with no history of hostility towards furniture. Mrs Nape remarked that she thought she had been up against a quite different character. I said this reply seemed to be based on complete failure to listen to what I'd said. 'When I'm in a temper,' responded Mrs Nape, 'it's not a pleasant sight. Well, there—I'm made like that. My late husband could have told you.' 'But he didn't. He couldn't,' I said, recklessly. It would be disastrous to be thrown out of the flat, but really this old lady was imposs-ible. For answer, she began to tell me her life story. It grew like some hideous plant, tendril by tendril, vexatious detail by detail, till it covered the afternoon . . . and I heard Kate and Tom stirring above us. 'I hope we understand each other,' I said, rising. 'No one pulls the wool over my eyes,' said Mrs Nape. 'When I'm in a temper . . .'

I stumbled upstairs.

So Ben and Marie and Kate and I were lying on the edge of the cricket field opposite the flat, as far as possible from Mrs Nape's inexplicable inflammations. I was looking up into layers of burning leaves, imagining myself pinned to the roof of a vast blue abyss, in which birds were flying upside down.

'Lots of Dr Banana's boys, I suppose,' my mother had said that morning, having asked about my pupils. I was telling Ben about this : he having been from boyhood a collector of mother's . . . creative inexactitudes. To her, she'd told him once, bad manners were 'like a wet rag to a bull'. And overhearing our talk about one of our teachers, an arrogant man, she'd said : 'Oh, he thinks he's the cock's whiskers !'

I'd just had a letter from the London County Council. They'd thought again about my war service, and had decided to raise my salary to £444.15s. It might carry us through, with a few hair-raising moments when we reached the year's financial rapids. Ben said it would perhaps make sense to amalgamate our separate quests for houses. They were tiring of their maisonette, which would be too small, anyway, once their expected child arrived. We clearly couldn't live much longer over Mrs Nape's crazy head. Should we rope in another and look for some big old house that would convert into flats, with a garden on the same scale that our children could grow up noisily in?

I told Ben of one of my father's latest remarks. 'Young Fletcher's becoming more human! Surprising what a wife and a child-to-come will do . . .' I'd rashly asked him what kind of failure to be adequately human he'd detected in Ben. Had he been inhuman, or subhuman, or superhuman? My father said he'd been inclined to play about cleverly with words, a habit that either he'd passed on to me or I'd passed on to him. He hoped Ben would be smothered in children and that Marie would see that he got out in the garden at weekends.

But how touchingly gentle my father was with Tom! Towards his grandson his softness was utter, a doting quality. In it I saw the way I must have been treated myself as a child—such a mixture of tremendous tenderness and . . . oh, that hardness, always ready to take over. Was there ever such a tender hard man?

Ben said here we were, thirty years old: persons without any background that really belonged to us. We'd have to create for ourselves a setting and an entire way of life.

I told him how Ruffett had suddenly beaten the mildest boy in Potts's class, probably the mildest boy in the school. The class had poured out into the hall and away, after a roaring lesson, and this boy had been simply the only one to walk and not to run: so he'd been caned, when it came to it, for unique innocence. He'd wept bitterly, and I'd been reminded of an incident when Ben and I were walking in Hereford, two years before. On a hilltop a rabbit, caught round the body by a snare, was running in frantic circles. When we appeared, it began to circle even more wildly, its eyes immense with terror. I'd felt desperately in my rucksack for a pair of nail scissors: Ben had taken them and stepped across to the snare. 'It's wire,' he called. At that moment, the rabbit fell on its side, panted; and then, its whole head swollen with fear, lay twitching. While I put the scissors back in my pack, Ben hurried on; and when I caught him up, we said nothing more about it.

Did I want to join a profession of which Ruffett was a member?

Ben asked what my verdict was now on the year at Isleden, looked at from Savage Street. I said in those few weeks the training college had been virtually wiped out of memory. It

178

seemed as little relevant as, say, having learned to knit as a preparation for being a dustman. Coming away from Savage Street, I'd feel that I'd spent the day in a dustbin. Bing had rung a few nights before: unrecognisably downcast. Where was the Professor Bing of Broom's invention—appointed to the Chaise Longue in Romantic Studies? Horrified to find himself slapping boys' faces: worst of all, the face of a boy of whose unhappiness at home he was well aware. We'd underestimated the dreadful social conditions we'd find reflected in the schools. Bing thought he'd soon cease to be a teacher—either because he'd given up, or because he'd been sacked.

What the training course did, alas, was to promote a general airiness, a special kind of mental grandeur, tied up with fine phrases and all those dilapidated references to Plato and Rousseau and Montessori. If Plato couldn't be brought alive, as someone who might himself teach in Eastbourne Road or Savage Street, then it might be best to leave him dead, for the moment, and force a student to create one or two ideas for himself and then fight for their existence. Something tough, anyway: because what was waiting for us was something *very* tough indeed. If you weren't made aware of that throughout the course, then the fall, when it came, from theory to fact could be stunning. It could start a teacher off on the wrong foot, with the prospect that he'd stay on it for a working lifetime. Sour, frightened, angry.

Oh, we'd been lucky, in the emergency course, the lecturers being, most of them, real working teachers, who'd recently been in the schools, and would soon be back in the schools; not men and women who made a career of teacher training, drawing on fainter and fainter memories of reality. But still, there'd been so much that, even now, so soon, I could see we'd not been given.

Tom, lying between Kate and Marie, was quarrelling with the grass. Kate was wearing the new summer frock we'd not been able to afford. There was net practice going on in a corner of the field, and suddenly it seemed thirteen or fourteen years earlier, and Ben and I lying in the field at the back of the school, talking of unimaginable futures—or more possibly of the only imaginable one, which had arrived punctually on 3 September 1939 . . .

Well, I said, there was this matter of a teacher having to

spend so much of his time being larger than life. It wouldn't
do for him to be a negligible character in his own classroom.
He couldn't, as people did in other jobs, keep himself to himself: duck away behind his work. He needed, I was beginning to
see, a trick or two for escaping from this overlargeness: from the
strain of having to be some sort of giant.

It was all manner of tricks I wished we'd been taught, or
encouraged to invent for ourselves.

Oh yes, grandeur! It wasn't a mean sort of job, after all.
But a tough, fighting grandeur!

5

Bickers, who had no trouble with the third year, was a garrulous
man ('I talk the kids into the ground'), who said the district
didn't worry him: he was a rough customer himself. He thought
I hadn't, at the moment, a useful classroom personality—not
for these classrooms, anyway. 'Too quiet and courteous.' In the
end, though, he said doubtfully, they might come to appreciate
me. He'd seen more surprising things.

Had recently married, himself. Could imagine I might have
the same defects, pardon him, as a husband as I had as a teacher.
'The great thing in my opinion is to make it clear at the start
that you mean to rule the roost.' Could guess I made a romantic
sort of husband. High-flown, rather. Pardon him. In his view,
you could adapt to being married to any woman, given physical
compatibility.

In breaks that were too short for bridge, the staffroom grew
hot with talk. Much of it was provoked by Gee, a communist,
with no gift as a debater: who, perhaps because he could never
get an argument off the ground, grew angry at the outset of any
discussion whatever. He'd jump up, shouting: 'It's time we had

a little socialism, isn't it?' Bickers would bellow, in return: 'Why don't these bloody communists go to Russia . . . If you offered them a boat to New York and one to Vladivostok, I know which one they'd choose.' 'You don't understand anything'—from Gee. 'The redistribution of wealth . . .' 'There's no wealth to redistribute in this country'—coolly from Bickers: who would add, 'Mind you, I've no strong views one way or the other.'

Among the ex-servicemen on the staff there was wry talk of being back, soon, in uniform. The *Evening Standard* shouted 50,000 DEAD IN SEOUL: the *Daily Worker* replied with 15,000 AMERICANS KILLED.

There was an elderly art master, a man longing for retirement, who let his classes trace Walt Disney figures—'Of course it's a worthless thing to do,' he said, 'but I'm not in the front line any more'. He spoke of the school as a prison, and made macabre jokes about our bunches of keys. 'So it's a bit shabby,' Bickers would say. 'So are we all. I don't care.' I was amused by a contribution to a discussion of this sort, on one occasion, by a man with a youngish face who came from a family of teachers: a quiet sensible man: to whom our disorders were particular forms of traditional difficulty, to be tackled with professional calmness. I thought—feeling he was a touchstone of something or the other—that in some sense Smith was the only real teacher on the staff. He said, carefully, that the school was not too bad, considering the district: and he pointed out that the hall was unusually well-lighted.

I had a nickname: Tissuepaper. Croucher told me about it, companionably. 'Like it, sir?' There was a suggestion of my being able to ask them to go back to the drawing board, if I wasn't pleased.

Punter, a dangerous-faced boy in the top year and a member of the school's worst family, suddenly went for Ruffett with a knife. Ruffett drove him to the ground with sheer bulk and then held him there with his heavy foot. The headmaster—actually *far* too gentle for the place, I was beginning to realise—was persuaded to exclude the boy from the school.

It certainly solved the problem that Punter represented to his teachers—always, under his bitter provocations, likely to attack and be attacked. But it was no solution of Punter's own problem: and obviously an exacerbation of the problem he was, and would continue to be, for the rest of the world. It had happened before, with other Punters. The school washed its hands, but left others to dirty theirs.

In the playground those top year boys looked to me like violent scarecrows. I was sent in to them twice, when my own boys were doing Art. Of the first occasion I retained, five minutes after it was over, only a shocked memory of numbers being chanted, on an ascending scale of noise, for minutes on end: and of what happened when I told a boy to stop chewing: the whole class began chewing, and kept it up till the bell rang. The second occasion made me aware that what I thought of as a gallantly humorous response might be of no help at all. On the blackboard, as I entered, a word, hugely written. It was a word intended to shock if not to alienate. I said: 'Will the boy who wrote his name on the board come and rub it out.' They were dumbfounded, and then . . . hilariously solicitous. They offered to take me through the register to demonstrate that there was no one in the class of that name.

My humorous stroke had failed because they believed I was genuinely unfamiliar with the word. Instead of my wit being acclaimed ('Good sport, sir!'), my innocence and ignorance were deplored.

After which they formed a scrum and removed a boy's trousers, informing me that it was an activity much encouraged by their form teacher. 'Be more fun if this was over in the girls, eh, mister?'

It was a relief, always, to be shut in with my nineteen. During an arithmetic lesson, Furr and Dunkin told me about the local rackets. Largely a matter of coming into possession of objects without having paid for them, and finding customers for them who were out of touch with the current going rate for anything. Best if there were no more than five minutes between the two transactions . . . 'So he makes a quid for himself, see,' said Furr. 'On top of the other quid,' said Dunkin.

Well, it was a sort of arithmetic . . .

I couldn't bear the school dinners: they were brought in daily from some distant kitchen, having time to become infinitely old and cold. The worst seemed to have been cooked in an unclean cloth : and there was much enclosing of elusive rags of meat in pastry inches thick.

I went, instead, down into Kings Cross, and ate in an ABC full of muttering tramps. I'd fallen into the habit of wandering afterwards through the station : in a melancholy way, liking the atmosphere of cross-country arrival and departure : staring at the sweating black engines that yesterday were in Edinburgh or York.

I was looking now very closely at the dilapidation of things— wondering, because my horror was so great, if I'd exaggerated. The black houses from which my blackened boys came. The great tenements, built by philanthropists—the children pouring in and out of their arched entrances looking like rioting mobs. 'It is terrible,' I wrote in my diary, 'that we should allow anyone to become as thin and pale and gaunt and worn and ugly as an old woman I saw at the door of one of the black, broken-windowed houses.' *Black*. It was the word. 'The withdrawal from the inhabitants of Kings Cross of all pleasant opportunities and all hope of development makes me want to cry out loud. The young girls with their parodies of fashionable dress—and even their dresses greasy and stained . . . I want to be able to sweep the whole horror into a gigantic dustheap.'

I'd written to Mr Salt, telling him that I was clearly going to be this sort of loose item on the Savage Street staff, or one like it, after the summer holidays and then as far forward as my masters cared to peer. Mr Salt replied at once :

'To be supernumerary is not very good, of course—incentives are lacking, nothing can be developed, improvisation is all very well. A hand-to-hand life when you really want to be getting your teeth into a job with some continuity about it. However, super-numerary status at Savage Street is better than permanency there . . .'

He wasn't surprised by my horrified view of the district.

'I know the effect of that area : even to walk through it un-moved you have to be a robot—or a native who has never seen anything else. I know the helpless feeling that can come from battling with all the odds of dirt, staleness, sheer ugliness, dulled senses, senses sharpened in the wrong direction.

'But, strangely enough, compensations come and despair edges

183

back—I have found it so and you will, I am sure. Give the lads time to accept you . . .'

I found myself continuing, at every odd moment, to read Donne and think about him, discovering in him some source of strength for use in Savage Street. Well, it didn't make sense if the best were not related to the worst. It didn't make sense to read poetry or hear music as if these things existed in some other world than the one in which Kings Cross existed. That's what had been wrong with Isleden : the many formal separations it went in for, between the great and the petty, the ideal and the real : Jepp and Trellis : serious and solemn : work and leisure . . . Yes, damn it : as to that last—wasn't it in the schools that we taught this false distinction bewween grey work and gaudy freedom from it? Couldn't we make work itself gaudy?

'. . . indeed,' I scribbled, 'that idea of a poem beginning like a pistol-shot is not inapposite : for much of his early poetry (and indeed much of his later work, when God replaced his "profane mistresses") is a kind of war. Donne is the angry soldier among love-poets, fighting to harmonise the difficult laws of body and mind. He does not set up, and worship, an ideal woman. He is not a realist, of the kind that believes the worst about life : on the other hand, he is not an idealist of the kind that chooses to invest life with a general cloudy glory. He sets the bad and the glorious side by side : the "paine and shame" and the "happy dreams" : and if we find that the truths he wrings from this conflict are indeed glorious, then we must admit that their glory is a hard, admirable glory, gained by facing the actual and not by celebrating the imaginary.

'His poetry is in the profoundest sense autobiographical : we always feel that a poem of Donne's springs from a living experience, like an entry in a diary. Rather than emotion recollected in tranquillity, we have emotion recorded in a superb agitation. How often we have longed to know how Donne wrote, to confirm our feeling that he did indeed write poetry as one would write a diary, in obedience to an immediate hot impulse and not after a period of reflection and germination. It is because he wrote like this, or gives the impression of having written like this, I think, that we experience in his presence an intense excitement. The occasions that give rise to his poems seem still to exist, to belong to our troubled world in which, like him, we seek to make sense of a mass of disparate incidents and thoughts.'

Well, all that use of 'we' apart, which I then thought was an indispensable item of critical language (it was like throwing your arms round the shoulders of, oh, half a dozen of the leading literary scholars), this *was* the feeling Bing and I had had, at the beginning of the Isleden course, when we stared in the Tate Gallery at those paintings by Velasquez. Because of the way he worked, the moment at which the Infanta Margarita Teresa stood for him, hands lying on the immense panniers of her skirt, seemed still to exist, like the occasions that had given rise to Donne's poems. No older, no newer, than this morning, when Croucher had written for me, in what amounted to a foreign language, two pages of what he assured me was intimate reminiscence ('All about my auntie and that') : which had filled me with the pleasure of schoolteaching : and Walker had shouted at me obscenely, for reasons which I did not begin to understand, and I'd struck him, which had emptied all the pleasure out. I felt, then, trapped for life in a world of innumerable Savage Streets.

The fine weather had broken, and a wind blew that sounded like someone bursting envelopes, followed by huge blowsy rain : all the black dust had become black puddles. Ruffett told me the Head was henpecked, and Bickers, curious why I looked so astonished, said : 'He'd talk scandal to a fourth year boy, if there was no one else.' It was Kate's birthday : she was thirty, and I'd be thirty in nine days' time. 'That's going to be our trouble . . . This great difference in our ages. When you're forty I shall only be thirty-nine.' I didn't believe, of course, that we should ever be forty.

And Tom was a golden web of hair and a spread of fingers. Sucking a thumb had become his occupation, intently pursued. Lately he'd discovered his penis, but had tired of it, finding it had the great defect that you couldn't throw it away and command it to be retrieved. We'd got over our feeling that we'd never see so fragile a creature through his first year. Only one sentence of Dr Spock's manual on child-rearing, we'd concluded, had much value : 'Your baby is tougher than you think.'

They'd given out reports that afternoon, and when I made my way home Savage Street was white with the fragments of them. The term would come to an end the following day, and after six weeks there'd begin the first of the hundred terms that, presumably, lay ahead.

Thoughtlessly, finding her waiting as I got off the bus, I mentioned to Kate something I'd just read—a forecast by Bertrand Russell of an imminent ten years' war, a nuclear Troy. And so, on that July evening in 1950, we walked through the wet world silently: while our son, in his pram, turned his small face this way and that, taking in the enormous amazement of it all.